STRATEGIC ASSET MANAGEMENT

The Quest for Utility Excellence

STRATEGIC ASSET MANAGEMENT
The Quest for Utility Excellence

Clive Deadman

Matador
5 Weir Road
Kibworth Beauchamp
Leicester LE8 0lQ, UK
Tel: (+44) 116 279 2299
Email: books@troubador.co.uk
Web: www.troubador.co.uk/matador

ISBN 978-1848763-661

A Cataloguing-in-Publication (CIP) catalogue record for this book
is available from the British Library.

Typeset in 12pt Sabon by Troubador Publishing Ltd, Leicester, UK
Printed and bound by TJ International Ltd, Padstow, Cornwall, UK

Matador Business is an imprint of Troubador Publishing Ltd

Contents

ABOUT THE AUTHOR

Clive qualified as a chemist and worked in Africa for the mining industry, before moving into the venture capital arena. Over an eight year period, he invested in, and became a director of, several engineering businesses.

On joining the utility sector, his long interest in asset management was fuelled by his desire to understand the value that utilities receive from operating and investing in their regulated assets.

In 2002, he sponsored the implementation of Condition Based Risk Management (CBRM) into UU Electricity. In 2007, this application won the 'Innovation in Engineering Award' and helped move the business from the lower to the upper quartile of Ofgem's regulatory efficiency and performance ranking.

United Utilities' capital maintenance or asset management proposals for water and waste water, which Clive has implemented or managed, have consistently been recognised in the UK regulators' 2004 and 2009 price reviews as representing upper quartile asset management capability.

Clive is a member of the council of the Institute of Asset Management and the European Federation of Maintenance Societies. He also chairs the Investment forum for the UK's Energy Innovation Centre.

He lives in Cheshire, England, with his wife, two children, three dogs, four chickens and a cat called Charlie.

Foreword

This book covers an important topic in a vital sector.

The critical services provided by utilities are essential to the fabric of modern society; and the case studies within this book provide strong evidence to show how vital good asset management is and will make you think hard about its development.

A novel capability framework for asset management is explored in the book. For those readers well practiced in asset management, this capability framework will both complement and challenge your current thinking. For those readers less practiced in asset management, this capability framework will emphasise how successful asset management requires the integration of many different business functions and disciplines.

I commend this book to those of you wishing to gain insight into the application of asset management in the utilities sector.

Robert Davis
President of the Institute of Asset Management

Dedicated to George Eric Deadman

Businessman, traveller, and a real rocket scientist.

Preface

The quest for utility excellence

This book is important for us all because utilities are the foundation stones of civilisation and asset management systems are at the heart of any utility. A good asset management system allows a utility to manage risk and value and a great asset management system allows excellent business performance.

I have prepared this book by drawing on my personal experience of running utility business and the cumulative wisdom of leaders of utilities who own and operate over £750 billion of electricity, water, wastewater, gas, rail and power generation utility assets and provide services to 300 m customers.

This book illustrates the numerous paths to asset management excellence which have been successfully used by leading utilities and utility leaders across the world. It does so by drawing on numerous case studies of great successes and setbacks that ambitious utility businesses and leaders encountered as they sought progress and improvement. As I have charted this path to excellence I have illustrated the strategies and principles which allow utility leaders, regulators and operators to find the answers to the following three questions:

- How good must an asset management system be so it adds more value than cost?
- How can such an asset management system be implemented?
- How do great utilities ensure their asset management system earns the confidence of the board of the company and all the core departments?

However the path to excellence never ends. Although this book details solutions and approaches which have been proven to be successful by leading utilities the great utilities are those which have the ambition to seek to achieve levels of excellence what have not been achieved before.

I am told many of the business issues and approaches discussed in this book have great relevance to other asset-intensive industries and complex activities, such as healthcare provision.

Clive Deadman
March 2010

Acknowledgements

I have been inspired to write this book by my father. Shortly before he died he mentioned a few things he would have liked to have done if time had permitted. I have since learnt ninety per cent of people over the age of 70 wish they had taken more risk in their life. So when I felt I had an opportunity to write this book, I decided to take the plunge.

I would also like to thank my colleagues at United Utilities some of whom I have worked with to address challenging business issues, and others who more recently have reviewed and contributed to the book. Although there are far too many to be able to acknowledge I would like to thank Martin Bradbury, Graeme Sims, Eoin Cooke, Dave Champness, Tricia Williams, Garry Edwardson, Mark Abbott, Peter Mahon, Bob Emerson, Mark Preece, Sandra Featherstone, Karen Miller, Tim Fynn, and Eddie Hamilton and Mike Kay, now of Electricity North West.

Particular thanks are also due to the Institute of Asset Management, and so many of its members. It has been great working with them and understanding the capabilities and challenges they all face in their very different industries. Particular thanks are due to Ursula Bryan (for leading the Institute's formal review of the manuscript) and David McKeown for numerous discussions from the start to the finish of this project. I hope this book is one more small step towards our goal of helping people from many different backgrounds to understand the depth of the challenge and the exciting opportunities that face us.

Without the sponsors of the book, this project would never have been possible. Preparing and researching this book has not been particularly expensive, but without the very early offer of financial support from these sponsors I could not have contemplated funding the cost of the worldwide travel and accommodation which researching and putting a book on the shelves entails. Accordingly, my particular thanks to Theo Quick and Yvonne Guice of Logica, George Butler and Martin McIlwaine of Northern Ireland Water, Robert Davis and Paul Barnfather of EA Technology, Denis O'Leary and Kevin Niall of ESB Networks and Martin Sedgwick of Scottish Power.

My thanks to the numerous utility staff, consultants, experts and regulators who have given the project so much help and advice. In particular, I should like to thank the staff at the following companies who have supported the project in one manner or another.

Barrie Hydro
Electricity North West
Hydro One
Scottish Power Energy Wholesale
Northern Ireland Water
Severn Trent Water
Abu Dhabi Distribution Company
London Underground
Yorkshire Water
Northern Gas Networks Limited
United Utilities
Southern Water
ESB Networks
Logica

BC Hydro
Scottish & Southern Energy
Scottish Power Energy Networks
EA Technology
Abu Dhabi Sewage Services Company
Anglian Water
National Grid
E.ON
Tube Lines
Reynolds Partners
Scottish Water
Thames Water
Transco (UAE)
Scotia Gas
South West Water

The book has also greatly benefited from the advice and support from many from all corners of the world. In particular, I am grateful for the support of Dr. Penny Burns of AMQI in Australia.

From the very outset I have sought, and immensely benefited from, the advice of the book's editorial panel, composed of Geoff Aitkenhead of Scottish Water, Chris Newsome of Anglian Water, Dean Fathers of IDM group and Jeremy Bending of National Grid. Together they have managed to find time in their demanding schedules to review sections of the book as it has taken shape, and challenged and commented and given me a great deal of advice. I have not taken their advice on all points and, accordingly, all the faults, errors and omissions that remain are mine.

Thanks also go to John Melluish for building the first web site for free.

Finally, and most importantly, my greatest thanks to my wife, Wenda for giving me such support throughout the last 18 months.

1 Introduction

There is a fundamental transformation under way in many of our utilities across the world. Their growing complexity and the greater demands from customers for better service and value means traditional ways of working are unaffordable. This is important for all of us as utilities make up 5% of the gross domestic production of the world and just about everything else we value is wholly dependent on their reliability and effectiveness. The solution is to introduce ways of working which allow utilities to understand value and risk better, and so squeeze more value out of their utility assets. This book explores the approaches leading utility companies are using to improve their ability to manage their assets.

Most utilities have made a great deal of progress in the last 15 years in improving their asset management capability. Achieving excellent utility asset management is increasingly seen as a priority by key utility stakeholders, regulators and utility boards. Furthermore, the publication and broad acceptance of PAS 55[1] has been instrumental in creating a common language that is increasingly winning international acceptance. Nonetheless, many of the asset management systems that utilities use are implemented differently. This diversity is exciting and helpful. But many leading utilities are simultaneously seeking to address the same issues, and there is certainly a need for better sharing of best practice.

For reasons that will be explored later, utilities need to manage much greater risks than in the past and to a point, this trend is likely to continue. However, we need to take great care. Utilities are often taken for granted until something goes wrong. The failure of any utility system can quickly

---

[1] BSI PAS 55-1:2008 A publicly available specification of Asset Management developed by the Institute of Asset Management (IAM) in collaboration with the British Standards Institute (BSI). ISBN: 978 0 580 50975 9

lead to immense personal and economic damage. An extended failure of utility services quite quickly makes urban areas unviable.

Many people, perhaps, think they already understand the utility sector because they assume it is a simple business or, as service consumers, they have a false sense of familiarity. Within utilities themselves, meanwhile, many have worked for the same utility business for years so perhaps don't realise that most people know so little about what they do. But this lack of understanding can be dangerous, particularly as there is such a fundamental change underway in our utilities at present.

In recent years a greater focus on safety, flood and explosion risks, new environmental standards and climate change have prompted huge levels of investment into utility assets. Policy makers in government are also looking for utilities to fund other initiatives, such as new flooding or climate change issues, or the use of preferential tariff regimes to accommodate the most vulnerable. However, there is a limit to the amount of debt and range of issues that utilities can carry. Not only must the confidence of governments (and sometimes investors) be maintained but customers must also be prepared to pay current and future utility bills.

Pressure has been rising on the utility sector for some years to do 'more with less'. Once the quick wins from early efficiency improvements are realised by utilities across the world, attention increasingly moves to more strategic approaches to drive out further effectiveness and efficiency. Those strategies include privatisation, consolidation, nationalisation, regulation, competition and sub-contracting to stimulate higher levels of performance from utility organisations. Utility managers have a role to deliver these transformational changes while ensuring essential services are not interrupted.

Inside our utilities and infrastructure businesses there are other more fundamental pressures building up. In the mature economies, much of the utility infrastructure is old and nearing the end of its life. Utility operators must find ways to contain asset risk while simultaneously rebuilding and transforming the effectiveness of utility equipment. In the younger economies, utility provision is frequently a political issue – access to utility services is increasingly seen as a right for individuals and for corporations and improved infrastructure services in a region drives economic growth. Utility managers in these younger economies are seeking to keep ever-more complex utility networks operating while extending services to large numbers of new customers.

As a result, there is now a revolution underway in many of our utilities. Historically, the only way a utility could be managed was through local managers drawing on their personal knowledge of the assets and processes in their neighbourhoods to operate the system. Activity was controlled by constraining the levels of resource made available (generally, money), often on an annual basis. While this can be effective in times of plenty, it is not efficient and it makes it impossible for customers, managers and regulators to understand if they are getting good value.

Thirty years ago, utilities started to recognise there was a need for a new way of working within their business that ensured efficient levels of investment were available to deliver effective services sustainably. In time, this new way of working became known as 'Asset Management' and in order to operate in these different ways a utility needs to establish an 'asset management system'. The Institute of Asset Management defines the asset management system as[2]:

> *Systematic and coordinated activities and practices through which an organisation optimally and sustainably manages its assets and asset systems, their associated performance, risks and expenditures over their lifecycles for the purpose of achieving its organisational strategic plan.*

A number of elements in utilities' asset management systems have been used for many years. What has changed is the complexity of modern asset management systems, with oversight of the whole system becoming more important. Not all utilities require a formal

[2] The Institute of Asset Management, www.theIAM.org

asset management system, however. A changing business climate and the greater complexity of utility systems means it is less likely an organisation can leave the asset management system to run itself.

Operating an asset management system requires an objective understanding of a number of difficult issues, such as the real and acceptable levels of risk, customer value for money, affordability and availability of new interventions, and operational cost and capital investment 'trade-offs'. The task of deciding what is necessary and good value becomes more difficult because there are many people who need to use similar types of information and data, while others may create data accidentally as they go about their work.

Only in the last few decades have utilities been able to implement joined-up asset management systems. Thirty years ago, much information was held in individual's heads, and where central records existed they were invariably individual works of art, drawn on paper and held in a local archive or drawing office. At that time, the only computers were used for payroll and billing, and any calculators were mechanical hand-operated machines. More recently the growing availability of information processing techniques has enabled utilities to collect and formalise the types of asset information they hold and make it available to many different users.

Although many utilities have a department called 'Asset Management' almost everyone in a utility manages assets in one way or another, and so has an essential role to play in the asset management system. Accordingly, as the asset management system evolves and matures, roles and types of work will change. Necessary changes have included new options for organisational design and fundamental changes to business processes, investment planning and asset and business risk management. Managing these changes – and the associated people and cultural elements – are undoubtedly the greatest challenges facing utilities. A highly experienced utility manager once explained to me:

> *The introduction of modern information systems is really*
> *quite simple. It only needs one of two things – either*

someone with great vision, or a huge disaster. The only question is which arrives first.

These new and imaginative concepts, improvements in information processing capabilities, new options for supply chain management and the internet have transformed how utilities operate. And this process has just started. It is likely change will continue for another 20 years as asset management capabilities grow and become more widely adopted and deeply applied. And there are many new issues ahead of us. The adoption of smart metering and smart grid technologies alone could, in theory, result in the utility sector handling more meter data than all the information that currently passes over the internet today!

These improved asset management capabilities allow us to predict and manage the future performance of utility assets. As a consequence, utilities have the option of moving from a reactive to a more proactive and planned way of working. This capability is crucial for regulators and political leaders who quite rightly demand the proof that utilities need the funding they ask for, particularly if it means less investment is available for more visible and popular projects, such as building hospitals and schools.

Since I began managing water, electricity and waste water utility businesses, I have been struck by the range of challenges a utility faces on this journey. In practice, any utility has an almost endless range of investment and operating options, each of which will be championed vigorously by someone. All these options will have merit, and benefits. However, only a few will be good value for customers. Accordingly, in order to manage risk and value, a practical and strategic approach to asset performance, cost and risk information is essential. Getting this right is one of the most commercially important, difficult and, at times, mundane tasks imaginable. On one hand, it is easy to design complex asset management systems that need asset data of a quality which is not available. Such systems may provide detailed information which may be plausible but unreliable. At the other extreme, a full data set for any utility's entire asset base would bankrupt it many times over.

Another key issue that must be respected and recognised is the exceptional commitment and passion which utility staff the world over share. People working in utilities know just how important and worthwhile their jobs are. I have seen people who might not respect their manager or even care particularly for their organisation, risk their lives in times of crisis to ensure services to customers are protected and maintained. This passion and belief give utility organisations immense energy, but it can also make the design and implementation of appropriate asset management systems more challenging.

The creation and development of these new utility asset management systems are also critical if we are to maintain the knowledge and skills of utility businesses. The new environmental and technical challenges attract many young people into the industry. But, naturally, even as this happens, many of our most experienced engineers and experts approach retirement and take with them decades of un-documented and irreplaceable experience and know-how. It is critical we ask them to help us shape and inform our asset management systems while they can. In future years, this will mean tomorrow's experts can build on the expertise we enjoy today.

While preparing this book, I have drawn on my experience in implementing and managing a range of asset management systems in the electricity, water and waste water sectors in Europe and the Middle East. In addition, I have visited a wide range of business leaders running different utilities throughout the world. My colleagues in these utility and infrastructure businesses have kindly shared case studies of lessons learnt, which have been used to illustrate and bring to life many of the points explored in this book. In all cases, the examples used are anonymous unless material has been published in the press or online by the organisation named.

Two-thirds of the utilities that have contributed material are based in North Western Europe and the remainder are located in the Middle East and North America. Sectors included are gas distribution and transmission, water treatment and distribution, sewage treatment and drainage, electricity transmission and distribution. A small number of examples from power generation and rail companies are also included. Figure 1.1 characterises the types of utilities involved.

In addition to appealing to experienced utility leaders who may be looking for fresh ideas or perhaps a broader view of these industries, I hope this book will prove both interesting and useful for people who are new to the industry. Accordingly, I have included three chapters at the beginning of the book that summarise the history of utilities, utility regulation and, finally, give an insight into the scale and nature of modern utilities. These introductory chapters will make the latter parts of this book more comprehensible to those readers.

I am also keen to explore in this book how good an asset management system needs to be. Across the world, utilities have different asset management capabilities and different appetites to develop more sophisticated asset management systems. Given this range of approaches, who is 'right'? How does a utility decide the necessary capability of its asset management systems?

Another issue for utility leaders and stakeholders is to decide how an asset management system should be implemented. All utilities need an appropriate asset management system, but not all utility businesses need a formal one. A small utility that provides a range of services to the residents of a small town, for example, may operate in a different regulatory climate than a large privatised water utility.

Figure 1.1 Types of infrastructure companies participating in the research

Utility sector	Number of companies	Population served (millions)	Utility asset replacement value (£ billions)
Waste water	11	57	302
Electricity transmission and distribution	13	89	201
Water	11	46	137
Gas transmission and distribution	4	81	62
Other infrastructure	2	22	78
Total	**41**	**296**	**780**

If a utility is under local government ownership and regulators, managers and political stakeholders – the decision makers – feel they have the appropriate experience of important issues, there is less need for a formal asset management system. However, informal asset management systems are also vulnerable to the retirement of key staff or to becoming beholden to the opinions of key individuals or stakeholders. Claiming to have an informal asset management system can also become an excuse for not having a proper asset management system at all!

A final question that this book seeks to answer is how the right systems can be designed and commissioned. Good asset management systems do not happen by accident. They require great leadership, commitment and vision if they are to be shaped and implemented into a utility business. To be successful, issues such as culture, organisational design and behaviours must be understood and managed.

There are six factors that shape the appropriate type of asset management capability for different types of utilities. These six factors are introduced in Chapter 5 and the subsequent chapters address each of these issues in turn. Three of these factors – climate, complexity and goals – determine the type of asset management system that is most appropriate. The second three factors – tools, organisation and teams – enable the asset management systems to operate effectively in the business. These six factors need to be in balance.

The character and relationship between these six factors is illustrated in the asset management capability model, shown in Figure 1.2.

This capability model is used throughout the rest of the book to illustrate the choices, techniques and pressures different utilities experience on their own efficiency and improvement journeys.

To put the asset management capability model into perspective, it is just one of a number of asset management models currently being used in different ways by the utility sector across the world. Some models are structured to follow asset life cycles and are useful

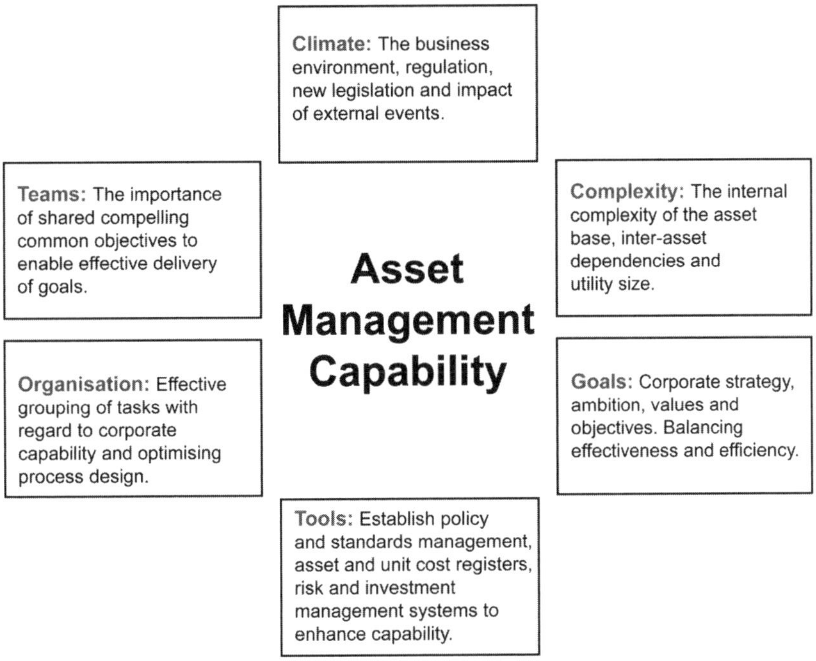

Climate: The business environment, regulation, new legislation and impact of external events.

Teams: The importance of shared compelling common objectives to enable effective delivery of goals.

Complexity: The internal complexity of the asset base, inter-asset dependencies and utility size.

Asset Management Capability

Organisation: Effective grouping of tasks with regard to corporate capability and optimising process design.

Goals: Corporate strategy, ambition, values and objectives. Balancing effectiveness and efficiency.

Tools: Establish policy and standards management, asset and unit cost registers, risk and investment management systems to enhance capability.

Figure 1.2 Types of infrastructure companies participating in the review

for process design while others map well onto organisational groupings or enable certification and benchmarking.

Much thought and care has been invested into many of these models; their different features allow them to be used in various ways to improve asset management systems and processes. The unique purpose of the asset management capability model, which is at the heart of this book, is to take a strategic view of the type of asset management system needed and the organisational and cultural approaches appropriate for its implementation. The asset management capability model can be used by utility organisations to answer the following three questions:

- How good does an asset management system need to be?
- How are great asset management systems implemented?
- How can the asset management system earn the confidence of the board?

With this clarity and consensus, utility experts have the support they need to build and operate effective asset management systems and utility leaders have confidence these systems are driven by the need for performance and efficiency.

In each of the chapters, I include an introduction and a conclusion. I have also attempted to summarise the chapters in these sections, which may be of value to readers with only a passing interest in certain aspects of utility asset management systems. I have also made extensive use of diagrams and tables to draw out key principles.

Before we start, a word of warning from a colleague of mine:

If you are managing a utility and you do not fully understand the asset risks, you may well be sleeping quite well at night. However, as you start to understand what might, could and probably is happening, you will no longer be able to do so. Until, that is, the time when you can quantify asset risk, performance and cost and you have a team managing those issues for you. It is only then that you will you be able to sleep well again.

2 The History of Utilities

2.0 Introduction

History shapes our world in countless ways. Take Chinese food – the nature and style of Chinese food today was determined by, of all things, the lack of timber in ancient times. With only grasses and sticks for kindling, meals were most easily prepared by cooking on brief yet hot fires. Chinese cuisine reflects this to this day.

Similarly, the history of utilities matters because it subtly influences today's business structures – the location, age and types of assets and the asset management systems needed to manage them.

For their part, the Romans and Greeks pioneered many techniques for treating and filtering water and delivering it to their urban populations in order to support their great cities. Many of their outstanding achievements were lost in the Dark Ages and so the techniques we recognise today had to be reinvented.

2.1 The Black Death

The impact of the Black Death, or 'the great mortality' as it was then known, illustrated the inability of medieval Europe and Asia to understand – let alone address – the threat of disease. It is believed that the Black Death originated in China around 1331 and moved westward along caravan and shipping routes. It arrived in the Crimea in 1346 and quickly spread across Europe in the following two years, first occurring in southern England in 1348. Geoffrey le Baker, an Oxfordshire monk, leaves one of the few surviving accounts of the passage of the disease:

> *Case Study 1: The Pestilence*
> *'As the grave yards did not suffice, fields were chosen for the burial*
> *of the dead...A countless number of common people and a host*
> *of monks and nuns and clerics as well, known to God alone,*
> *passed away. It was the young and strong that the plague chiefly*
> *attacked [...] This great pestilence, which began in Bristol on*
> *15ᵗʰ August and in London on 29ᵗʰ September [of 1348}, raged for*
> *a whole year in England so terribly that it cleared many country*
> *villages entirely of every human being.'*

The Black Death arrived in Scotland and Wales and 'laid it low' in 1349. It is also reported the plague:

> 'Scarcely touched the pure Irish who lived amongst the mountains and on higher ground, until the year of Christ 1357 when it unexpectedly and terribly destroyed them also everywhere'.

At a stroke, the Black Death reduced Europe's population by between 30% and 60%. Lack of effective drainage, sanitation and vermin control – the root causes – went unrecognised. Fearing contagion and 'foul air', the population shied away from the dead and crowded together in their attempts to avoid infection. Sadly, the rats moved with the surviving population to their various refuges and accelerated the spread of the disease.

Over the next three centuries, the Black Death was to return to Europe a hundred times.

2.2 Water and waste water (sewage) treatment

The sanitary benefit of clean water and sewage treatment would not be recognised for another 500 years, so monasteries and churches in medieval times were usually located upstream of villages to ensure that the powerful and influential had greatest access to untainted water. To this day, in North Western Europe, the more affluent sections of many towns and cities are to be found on the western sides, with industrialised areas located to the east. Presumably, the prevailing westerly winds ensured smoke, odour and nuisance were unlikely to upset the more influential residents. From the 1750s, some wealthy households began to use sand and charcoal filters to remove the unpleasant taste from drinking water.

Throughout the last 500 years during periods of urban re-development, visionary architects in London, Paris, Budapest and most major cities have taken the opportunity to establish basic, yet effective, drainage, to move rain water and sewage into the adjacent river. However, these works rarely improved sanitation for the bulk of the growing urban populations.

In 1830s London, general drainage and sanitation issues were still supervised by the Commissioners of Sewers, an administrative function that had been established around 300 years previously by King Henry VIII. Sewage drainage works were only funded by local rates, and low-lying areas closest to the river – which suffered the cumulative effect of foul drainage – held the poorest members of the population, who were least able to afford additional taxes. Most sewers were open ditches or, where they had to run underground, were wooden pipes, which often became blocked. When drainage works were deemed worthwhile, it was usually because foul flooding made commerce difficult or the sensibilities of the increasingly wealthy middle classes were offended.

The average life expectancy of a working-class male in London around this time was 19 to 23 years. Undoubtedly, poor food, hard work, foul water and crime all contributed to this situation and there were many calls for investment to address it. Unlike cattle, which had both value and an owner, if a working man was to die that was only his, or his family's, loss. Society's business case for improved sanitation was weak, and the benefits were unclear.

> *Case Study 2: Nineteenth-century health and safety practices*
> *Flora Tristan, a French writer, describes the appalling working conditions she observed in the 1830s at the Gas Light and Coke Company, London, in her Promenades Dans Londres:*
>   *'Two rows of furnaces on each side were fired up; the effect was not unlike the description of Vulcan's forge, except [...] the dusky servants of the English furnaces were joyless, silent and benumbed. [...] The foreman told me that the stokers were selected from among the strongest, but nevertheless they all became consumptive after seven or eight years of toil and died of pulmonary consumption. This explained the sadness and apathy in the faces and every movement of the hapless men.'*

Poor working conditions and unclean air, water and sanitation were tolerated as practical necessities but disease and epidemic alarmed the population at large. In 1817, cholera was first observed in Jessore, India. By 1823 it had spread to Russia and in 1831/2 it arrived in Paris. During the first month of the Paris epidemic, 9,000 deaths were recorded and there was almost immediate panic in London.

Towards the middle of the eighteenth century, significant investment in impounding reservoirs and simple public water distribution networks began to occur throughout London and the north west of England. Although the benefits of clean drinking water were partially recognised, the greatest driver for establishing such services was economic growth. In 1847, Manchester mill owners promoted the Manchester Corporation Water Act because they required a constant supply of water to power their mills. This act enabled the construction of the Woodhead and Arnfield Reservoirs, which guaranteed a flow of 121 million gallons of water a week. Once water had been used to power the new industrial processes, it was also available to provide water for the factory workers who were migrating to the newly industrialised areas of the north of England.

During the latter part of the nineteenth century, the greatest focus remained on the treatment and distribution of wholesome drinking water. Society was also beginning to recognise it must act on the sewage that was infecting river and surface water. Initially, drainage had been a low priority. Local issues were often addressed with specific projects so the workmanship and materials and equipment varied from project to project.

In the early nineteenth centuries in some wealthy European cities, the first forms of organised sewage treatments were established, consisting of 'sewage farms' where waste waters drained and 'night soil' (the contents of latrines) was taken by horse and cart. After settlement and drying on drying beds, the resulting humus was deposited on land at the sewage farms and allowed to compost, after which the land would be used to grow crops. In the north west of England – one of the first regions of the world to undergo industrialisation – many modern sewage works remain on the site of these original 'sewage farms', which were often located at a low-lying site close to a suitable river for discharging the foul waters. It is not unusual for old farm buildings dating back to 1830-60 to be used today as office accommodation or workshops for the modern treatment works.

It was not until 1854 that the cause of cholera was discovered by John Snow, with the help of Henry Whitehead, a minister. By identifying an infected London well that had poisoned the people using it, they demonstrated the link between cholera and drinking water contaminated by infected sewage.

As the causes of water infection became clearly understood, the provision of clean water and sanitation became a priority throughout the world – although progress was limited by the availability of funding.

In 1897, a chlorine bleach was used to disinfect a water main in Maidstone, Kent, in Great Britain, in the aftermath of a typhoid outbreak. It was the first recorded use of chorine in a public water supply. Chlorine's effectiveness in providing residual disinfection protection was quickly recognised throughout the world. The pace of improvement possible when funding is available is illustrated by events in North America. In 1900, there were 25,000 reported deaths a year from typhoid[1]. In 1908, chlorine was first used in North

America at the Boonton Treatment plant in New Jersey and by 1920 most urban dwellers in the US were safely consuming water disinfected with chlorine. The introduction of a bacteriological standard by the US public health service ensured minimum requirements were applied across the fragmented US water supply industry. By 1930, cholera and typhoid had been virtually eliminated.

This growing realisation that proper sewage treatment was vital resulted in a range of new sewage drainage and treatment practices being developed. Local water companies and municipal authorities invested in a range of ad-hoc extensions and modernisation works to their local sewage treatment plans and drainage systems. Before 1890, settlement of incoming sewage was practised to remove the bulk of contaminants before discharge back into water courses. By 1910, the 'biological method' of treatment was being promoted. Since then, a range of new techniques have been introduced in the US and Europe to settle out solids, remove grits, treat solids through dewatering, anaerobic digestion and subsequently composting, recycling to agriculture, or incinerating.

Treatment of the foul waters has been successively undertaken by secondary treatment, tertiary treatment and various forms of disinfection. Water and waste water treatment of any kind involves the movement of thousands of tonnes of water from process to process. Energy consumption and the use of different chemical and biological processes – which are sensitive to micro-toxins, weather events and temperature – meant engineering solutions were designed locally to allow water and sewage treatment plants and networks to make best use of the contours of the land on which equipment is located. The use of enormous concrete structures has made the repeated extension of treatment plants between 1910 and 2000 difficult and bespoke. As a consequence, the water and waste water treatment industries are poorly standardised and make use of a wide

---

[1] The Safe Drinking Water Act, regulations and Amendments by Edward J Calabrese, Charles E Gilbert and Harris Sastides, published by Lewis Publishers.

range of purpose-built and adapted systems and equipment.

Throughout Europe and North America the provision of water and waste water treatment was initially undertaken by numerous smaller companies. Consolidation has occurred in the UK and to a limited extent in North America. However, across most of Western Europe, the accountability for provision of water and waste water services remains fragmented. In France ownership and accountability for provision of services lies with the 13,500 water and 15,000 sewerage services. Notwithstanding the fragmented ownership of French water and waste water assets, a small number of national companies compete with local authorities to manage each of these separate services.

In Germany, where there are an estimated 7,000 water supply companies, geographical consolidation of utility services is more common. This is known as the Stadtwerke or Querverbund, which frequently manages electricity and gas distribution, district heating, water supply and waste water drainage for a city or town.[2]

2.3 Gas

The Flemish scientist Jan Baptist van Helmont (1580-1644) discovered that when coal and wood were heated, a material was created, which he named a 'wild spirit', since the concept of a gas was not yet understood. The potential for gas to be used for lighting was not recognised until the end of the eighteenth century, by which time, a number of high-prestige lighting projects across the world had been commissioned, including:

1783   Professor Jan Pieter Minckeleers' illuminations at University of Louvain, in what is now Belgium.
1787   Scotland: Lord Dundonald house lighting.

[2] Competition and Economic Regulation in Water, Tony Ballance and Andrew Taylor, IWA Publishing.

1792   London: William Murdock house lighting.
1797   Manchester: Manchester Police Commissioners' Offices
       entrance lighting.
1799   France: Philippe le Bon patented a gas fire.

The first commercial gas works was constructed in 1812 in Great Peter Street, London. It generated gas that was fed through wooden pipes to Westminster Bridge. In the US, the first gas plant was built in Baltimore in 1816, and in Germany the first plant was built in Hanover in 1825.

The provision of gas lighting had a transforming effect. Factories could operate night shifts for the first time, towns and cities became illuminated and social and public events of all sorts became possible in the evenings. By 1870, there were 340 gas works in Germany and by 1850, most small- to medium-sized towns in Europe and North America had a gas plant for street lighting. The invention of the 'gas mantle' in 1875 allowed gas flames to produce clear bright light and, in 1885, the gas pre-payment meter began to be used. The production and distribution of gas, however, was to remain a highly fragmented industry, poorly placed to compete effectively with the introduction of electricity in the early twentieth century.

In 1875, Herkimer County, New York, voted to invest $500 to lay gas pipes, buried just below the surface of the street, for street lighting. Although a gas lighter was employed at a cost of $40 a month, there were still complaints that the lights were not bright enough and were often not lit. In addition, the authorities struggled to prevent residents connecting their own properties to the public pipeline. In 1884, the county installed two carbon arc lights as an experiment. It worked, and, in 1884, the gas and certain electricity-generating assets from two neighbouring counties were merged to form Herkimer Light and Power.

Electricity was to prove hugely successful in lighting and powering machinery, yet gas, too, continued to show substantial growth as a heating fuel of choice. In the US, 50,000 town gas manufacturing plants of various sizes have been operated in the last

100 years. And in the UK, when the Gas Act 1948 came into effect, 1,062 privately owned and municipal gas companies were nationalised and merged into the twelve Area Gas Boards.

However, the cost and environmental effects of generating town gas from coal and the toxic nature of the product resulted in a decline in its domestic appeal. Accordingly the availability of cheaper and cleaner natural gas in the 1960-1980s was an important development for the modern gas industry. The move from town gas to natural gas had three significant implications for the old gas networks. Firstly, town gas was a damp gas, and the residual moisture kept the yarn and lead joints of older pipes damp and gas tight. With the introduction of natural gas, a dry gas, the joints have progressively dried out and become more prone to leaks. A second effect is that, because natural gas has a higher calorific value per m^3 of network capacity, the move to natural gas meant the capacity of the network was increased. As a consequence, the replacement of old gas mains can frequently be undertaken with a smaller pipe, which has allowed the development of a number of novel 'no dig' techniques to be pioneered in the gas industry.

In addition, the surplus capacity of much of the gas network has meant reinforcement of gas networks has not presented the same modernisation challenges as with other utility networks. Finally, and most significantly, the introduction of natural gas forced the gas industry to consolidate. This meant the closure of towns' coal gas plants and a centralised gas transmission structure imposed on a fragmented industry.

When the gas industry was later forced to embark on complex billing projects and asset registers – through a combination of the practicalities of customer service and a need to manage health and safety issues – the gas industry pioneered many asset management techniques. Many of these skills and information system concepts have since been carried into other utility sectors through the recruitment of gas industry staff and use of contractors.

Substantial increased efficiency and customer benefits have been possible by removing the need for different varieties of gas-generation process plant and standardising both the gas product and the new gas transmission networks.

More recently, replacing iron gas mains has become a priority for older gas networks across the world. In the UK, a long-term programme will see approximately 100,000km – or 50% of the network – replaced, concluding in 2032.

2.4 Electricity

Experiments with electricity were conducted throughout the eighteenth century, with many inventors pioneering various types of generally ineffective electric light bulbs. In 1879, Thomas Edison demonstrated and patented the first effective light bulb, a discovery that eventually led to the universal introduction of electricity as the dominant form of lighting.

Initially, electricity-generating companies were privately owned ventures.

Case Study 3: The Weaverham Electricity Supply Company
On 11th August 1913, the Weaverham Electricity Supply Company Ltd, based in Cheshire, England, sought an additional £5,000 of capital. The minutes from its First Annual Meeting of the Company, held that spring, give an insight into the pioneering nature of early utilities:

'...to continue the mains of the Company over a distance of four and three quarter miles to Cuddington and Sandiway, which will, when completed, make the mileage of the Company's Mains nine and three-quarter miles, and will provide sufficient sum to pay for Works Contracts, additions to Generating Plant, Buildings and Foundations, also purchase of additional land in conjunction with these extensions, and leave a working balance of £1,000. The Directors consider that the Districts of Sandiway and Cuddington offer exceptional possibilities taking into account the

number of houses and class of customer, also the absence of Gas competition'.[3]

'The Annual Report of the Electricity Supply Company Limited has been issued. We do not know whether it constitutes a record, but it is certainly remarkable for an Electric (Lighting and Power) Company to be able to declare a dividend of 5 per cent after the first year's working. The installation is on the overhead wire system, and the Company has applied for Statutory Powers.

'We beg to report that the Company has made a most successful start. The Engineer reports that although he had only estimated for 2,000 30 watt lamps, at the end of the year an equivalent of 4,791 have been connected to the Company's mains. [..] It is interesting to note that the number of consumers at the end of the first quarter was 20 with an aggregate of 800 lamps, while at the end of the year the number was 60 with an equivalent of 4,791 30 watt lamps.'

[3] Weaverham Electricity Supply Company Limited Prospectus and Subscription List, published 11 August 1913.

Growth in demand for electrical power continued across the world throughout the twentieth century, accommodated by continual extension and reinforcement of local lower-voltage networks. During the First World War, the economies of scale of large centralised power stations began to be recognised and higher-voltage electricity transmission networks were designed and built to transmit power to local networks. Many of these original power stations were to become the sites for later major power stations. Across Europe and North America, the successive consolidation of generating capacity, which occurred throughout the twentieth century, saw many of these sites replaced by key high-voltage transmission switching stations and transformers. Because power stations require large volumes of cooling waters, such sites are usually low lying, and close to water. As a consequence, to this day, many of the more critical electricity transmission network assets are located in low-lying sites close to water and vulnerable to flood risk and, in particular, climate change.

Transmission and distribution networks, however, remained highly fragmented. In 1914, there were 55 transmission systems operating in the US alone, and many thousands of local distribution networks[4]. There were similar problems in Britain and, in 1925, the British government asked Lord Weir, the Scottish industrialist, to solve the problem of Britain's inefficient and fragmented electricity supply industry. The result was the Electricity (Supply) Act 1926, which led to the creation of the Central Electricity Board with duties to establish a nationwide 132kv grid of high-voltage interconnections for use in emergency. These proposals were developed and extended step by step until, by 1938, the grid was operating as a national system.

In Europe, the damage done during the Second World War to power generation, distribution and transmission networks meant the private sector was unable to fund the replacement and repairs necessary. With the exception of Germany and Japan, where American influence prevailed in the immediate post-war years, European countries and the USSR adopted centralised power industries. In the UK, the 1947 Electricity Act resulted in the nationalisation of electricity generation, transmission and distribution industries[5].

In the period from 1950 to 1970, global growth ensured the swift expansion of electricity networks. But in the 1970s several factors – the OPEC embargoes of that decade, increasing concern over nuclear power safety and environmental issues, the higher cost of capital – slowed growth while power costs rose significantly. The figure below shows the age profile of the United Kingdom Electricity Distribution Network in 2006.

[4] US Bureau of Census.
[5] UK Electricity Networks, Scott Butler, Imperial College and Parliamentary Office of Science and Technology, September 2001.

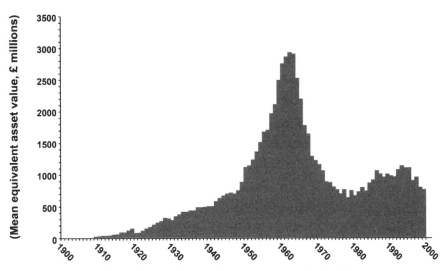

Figure 2.1 Electricity Distribution Network Age Profile (2004 cost base)

The relatively young age of electricity assets meant only low levels of basic maintenance work were necessary, as illustrated by Figure 2.2.

Although the North American power transmission network remains fragmented – it currently consists of 200,000 miles of lines

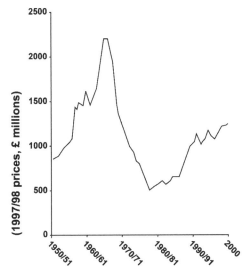

Figure 2.2 Ofgem Reviews of Public Electricity Suppliers 1998 to 2000 Distribution Price Control Review Final Proposals December 1999 p30

operated by 500 companies – a common feature of the European and North American networks is that they hold large numbers of network assets that are approaching the end of their useful life, while maintenance levels and network risk are also rising.

In the UK, the privatisation of the industry, a robust regulatory environment that has driven cost savings and the regulator-sponsored introduction of Geographical Information Systems have resulted in the consolidation of disparate paper asset registers into seamless data sets. For the electricity industry, network densities and the standardisation of equipment mean the benefits and challenges of this exercise are greater than they are for other network industries – and more complex than might be imagined.

However the digitisation of paper records is an enormous challenge. In the UK alone it is estimated 30,000 man years of work was needed just to transfer basic details of cable locations held on paper maps onto computer databases. Such exercises also require new ways of working, and the closure and consolidation of numerous regional drawing offices. In other parts of the world where this process is incomplete, the asset data legacy remains an impediment to modern ways of working and to further consolidation.

2.5 The development of Asset Management

After many years of relative stability, the higher cost of capital and the advent of inflation in the 1970s drove a new interest in finding better ways of funding utility and infrastructure businesses. It was not clear that the historical approach of managing activity by releasing funding was efficient or effective and, with many competing demands for funding, there was interest across the world in seeking better ways of working. It proved difficult to understand how value and risk were created because the operation, maintenance, replacement, funding and accounting of infrastructure businesses weren't integrated. Up until this time, utilities did not have asset registers, most records were paper-based, and computers were used largely for billing and payroll purposes only. As a consequence, there was little linkage between available funding and benefits realised by investing and maintenance activities.

In 1983, the first draft of the "True Cost of Services"[6], a paper that sought to understand the whole cost of providing water and waste water services in South Australia, including opportunity costs and current value depreciation, was published. This work led to a Parliamentary Inquiry in 1985 into the 'Cost and Timing of Asset Replacement' that covered all major state-owned infrastructure – electricity, water and waste water, transport, highways, hospitals, housing and schools and colleges on the same whole cost basis. The eight Parliamentary Reports (1986-1987) also covered accounting and funding aspects and, with their emphasis on the future renewal costs of assets, influenced the Public Sector Accounting Standards Board to adopt accrual accounting at all government levels across Australia as early as 1989.

In the subsequent 10 years a process throughout Australia and the UK of separating the management of infrastructure from the day-to-day control of the state led to significant efficiency and quality improvements. Where privatisation has also been undertaken, it has given this process a greater impetus but it has also added fresh challenges. A key element of this process has been the broader introduction of economic regulation and the strengthening of corporate governance. These issues are discussed further in Chapter 3.

In response to these pressures and in pursuit of efficiency gains, utility directors have sought ways to objectively and transparently demonstrate that asset risks are well managed and levels of funding are necessary, efficient and offer good value. During the last 15 years, the application of Asset Management principles has focused on developing techniques and approaches that ensure utility and infrastructure organisations can 'see' the value in everything they do. By balancing short and long-timescale operating and investment, as well as risk management pressures, these organisations are now becoming more able to provide effective services to their customers.

---

[6] Dr Penny Burns, info@amqi.com

2.6 Conclusions

Modern infrastructure services in Europe and North America remain fragmented or are composed of networks and treatment plants built to different design standards and operated as a patchwork of tiny independent operations and networks. This reflects the early focus of utilities to demonstrate effectiveness by connecting new customers and industries to utility services as quickly as practicable.

Figure 2.3 shows the numbers of separate utility organisations in England and Wales in 1947, following 50 years of consolidation.

By 1974, nationalisation policies had resulted in the consolidation of the UK's utility industries into a small number of large utilities. The recent development and expansion of national electricity networks and generation plant resulted in a degree of consolidation in these industries, too. In North America, outside the major cities, utility provision remains highly fragmented.

Water and waste water services were the first utilities to be made generally available. Initially, they were established to support growing urban populations and provide hydraulic power to new industries. However, as the causes of disease became better understood, such services became a priority while, across the world, national wealth determined the rate of improvement of water and sanitation. Initially, water and sanitation provision was highly localised. The nature of the processes involved, which require large civil structures and rely on

Utility type	Number of precursor utility companies
Water	171
Wastewater	1,564
Electricity	527
Combined electricity and gas	12

Figure 2.3 Numbers of separate utility organisations in England and Wales in 1947

gravity to enable drainage and flow, meant that the modern-day water and wastewater industries use many old assets, located at old sites. Standardisation is often poor, making the operation, maintenance and extension of treatment plants and networks more difficult.

The discovery that chlorine could be used as a residual disinfectant to treat and maintain the quality of drinking water resulted in its quick adoption throughout the world from the 1930s, saving enormous numbers of lives at modest cost. This practice may rank as one of the twentieth century's most effective and beneficial innovations.

The provision of gas was initially made possible by the construction of privately owned coking plants, which were constructed in most towns throughout Europe and North America in the nineteenth century. Town gas made from coal was replaced with natural gas during the twentieth century. This made the construction of long-distance gas transmission networks necessary and resulted in the closure of small local 'coking' plants and, in most cases, the formation of regional or national gas companies. The higher calorific value of natural gas effectively increased the network capacity of existing gas distribution networks, meaning that, in contrast to other utility asset bases facing modernisation challenges, the reinforcement of gas distribution networks has not been a major hurdle.

However, as this spare capacity becomes exhausted the need to reinforce the gas distribution network may well become an increasingly important factor in the future. The asset management systems required by the gas industry are less complex due to a number of factors – the relatively young age of the gas transmission network, the urban nature of the network and the adoption of a single strategy to address most asset risks (for instance, the outright replacement over a period of 20 to 60 years). The relative simplicity of these issues led to the gas industry pioneering the adoption of many modern asset management techniques, such as a requirement for asset registers, asset risk modelling, 'no dig' street working techniques and customer billing and trading systems. The movement of gas industry staff into other utility industries and the shared use of contractors mean these sectors have likewise adopted many of these approaches.

The provision of electricity started in the early twentieth century and quickly replaced gas for lighting and as a source of power for equipment. Local power stations were replaced by larger, more efficient power stations, which accelerated the construction of long-distance transmission and distribution networks. The relatively short lives of most electricity generation, distribution and transmission assets – just 50 to 60 years, usually – and the need to provide services with similar voltage and frequency means equipment has quickly become standardised. With the exception of buried lower-voltage cables, there are few very old assets remaining and, at first sight, fewer signs of the highly fragmented nature of early electricity networks. However, the routes of distribution lines and sites reflect the longer history of the industry, and many critical high-voltage assets are located on the low-lying sites of old power stations and are prone to flooding.

In addition, asset information held in registers is often structured and organised in different ways, depending on which drawing office maintained the records. The implications of this are quite fundamental and are considered later. Across the world significant numbers of assets built between 1950 and 1970 are all nearing the end of their lives at the same time. This imposes a critical and immediate need for electricity network operators to employ a highly effective capital maintenance planning capability. For these and other factors, many of the tools being developed by the electricity distribution and transmission industry will define the frontier of network risk planning and modern asset management systems. This is discussed in further detail later.

Utility history is frequently characterised by early periods of enormous expansion and growth, as operators and politicians seek to prevent huge loss of life from disease, underpin economic expansion and provide services demanded by the population. The initial provision of first-time services to affluent populations can be exciting, fashionable and profitable. However, as access to first-time services of all types becomes a 'right', utilities are required to provide the cheapest common standard of service and often face great pressure to restrict maintenance work and reallocate resources and connect customers to networks that are unable to accommodate them.

Throughout the twentieth century, between periods of growth and expansion, utility services have occasionally stagnated under government control. Annual funding reviews (where utility services must compete with more popular and visible public services for funding) can control and disturb levels of activity, which leads to poor planning and local areas of over- and under-funding. The advent of independent economic regulation and competition, which is discussed in the next chapter, has made new funding available and stimulated efficiency improvements. These new regimes, however, have also brought challenges as utilities find they must now work much harder to earn the trust of customers. The techniques utility businesses have adopted to respond to these new pressures and demands are explored in the rest of this book.

Varying degrees of consolidation of utility companies have occurred across the world. Thousands of very small utilities and private networks remain. Where utility consolidation has occurred, the physical nature of the utility networks and many of the underlying utility functions remain fragmented. Until 15 years ago, for example, even those utilities that consolidated into large groups held their asset records and plans in local offices. The extraordinary complexity and dispersed nature of utilities have made it difficult to manage value and risk effectively. Initial work undertaken 30 years ago in Australia questioned the traditional approaches to utility accounting and planning issues. In subsequent years, this subject, which became known as 'Asset Management', has broadened and deepened into all aspects of utility management.

The recent appetite for greater utility efficiency and effectiveness has led to the separation of utilities management from local government control, the empowerment of local utility managers and the introduction of regulation to drive higher levels of performance. In order to discharge their new responsibilities, utility managers and leaders are establishing the appropriate asset management systems in their businesses. Small and large utilities, however, face very different challenges and the remainder of the book will explore the different tools and approaches utility can use to tackle these challenges.

3 Utility Regulation

3.1 Introduction

This chapter reviews the essential features of the regulation of utilities' price and quality of service. The nature and tone of regulation is an important factor in determining the necessary capability of a utility's asset management system and these issues are explored in more depth in Chapter 6.

The need for regulation and its aims are influenced by political factors, national objectives and changing economic circumstances. Accordingly, this is a complex subject, one that is constantly developing and subject to continual debate. This chapter explores the principal characteristics of utility regulation so readers can understand the need for asset management planning systems of varying capabilities. The role of different types of regulators and the key regulatory approaches adopted in different countries are reviewed, although it is British utility regulation that receives particular attention, due to its long established application into many utility sectors. At the end of the chapter there is a short reading list of more comprehensive publications on utility regulation.

3.1 The purpose of regulation

Regulation is a process by which key public interest objectives of the regulated utilities are defined and a regime of penalties and rewards is introduced.

A degree of regulation is necessary when normal processes, such as competitive pressures, are not sufficiently effective to ensure the desired outcomes.

3.2 Types of regulators

Regulators can be broadly categorised into the following three types:

3.2.1 Economic regulators determine the prices that the utility may charge its customers, the scope of the services that must be provided and the level of profit that the utility can expect for good performance.

The independence of the economic regulator is essential but difficult to wholly maintain. Government may encroach upon the independence of the economic regulator which may result in the transfer of service and policy delivery from the state to utilities. For example, the provision of favourable utility tariffs to certain social groups or the high recovery of rates and other local government costs from utilities means utility bills are, in effect, used as a substitute for taxation.

Ineffective challenge of utilities by the economic regulator can result in high bills for customers and excessive utility profits. Excessive challenge of utilities will also result in utilities that are unable to recover their costs, and ultimately unable to fund essential levels of service. Accordingly, a difficult challenge for the economic regulator is to consult and challenge utilities, other regulators and government. At the same time, it must maintain objectivity and resist incorporating too many uneconomic or unconnected service requirements into utility service standards.

3.2.2 Quality regulators establish utility performance targets, such as environmental, health and safety legislation and drinking water standards, which create the need for new investment and new ways of working.

3.2.3 Customer champions represent the interests of customers, and frequently call for improved service standards and lower charges.

3.3 Regulatory approaches

Public ownership suits the character and objectives of mature utilities, which have a duty to provide basic services to all residents in an equitable manner. In the absence of effective competition or a mature regulatory regime, public ownership – and subsequent control through the democratic process – is the only practical option.

However, while public ownership is a good way of protecting the public from profiteering by private businesses, it is not in itself a strong model for promoting efficiency or innovation. Efficiencies that benefit customers[1] in the form of lower prices and/or better service are a result of separating management of utilities from management of the state, empowering and incentivising management to be more efficient and ensuring effective regulation.

Effective regulation, however, is not easy to achieve. In addition to ensuring regulatory independence, a policy commitment to liberalisation and a willingness to address other issues that could conflict, such as a desire to protect 'national champions', are necessary. There is also a requirement for well-developed financial markets.

A considerable information and power imbalance exists between regulators and utilities. The regulator has all the power and the utilities have all the information. It mirrors the imbalance that exists within the utilities themselves, where operational staff know which work needs to be done but it is the managers who set the budgets and overtime allowances. By implementing appropriate asset management systems that allow asset performance, risk and cost to

---

[1] Lecture titled 'A review of Privatisation and Regulation Experience in Britain', 7 November 2000, given as part of the Beesley Lectures: Lectures on Regulation Series X 2000' organised by David Currie of the London Business School and Professor Colin Robinson of the IEA.

be understood, managers, directors and regulators can discuss and establish the appropriate levels of service, funding and budgets. Accordingly, the asset management system must be designed and implemented with the needs of the regulatory process and the nature of the utility network in mind.

There are two types of economic regulation (Incentive-Based Price Setting and Rate Setting) and one type of competitive form (Concession) of price setting. Each of these mechanisms is discussed briefly below.

3.3.1 Incentive-Based Price Setting

This type of regulation allows utilities to increase prices by an amount linked to inflation, less an assumed future efficiency challenge. For this reason, this type of regulation is sometimes referred to as 'RPI-x' regulation, where 'RPI' is the UK Retail Price Index and the 'x' factor represents a percentage reduction in prices attributable to future efficiency savings. This allows customers to receive lower prices from the successive application of 'x' factors.

Utilities are incentivised to exceed targeted performance – for a period of time they are entitled to keep a proportion of any extra savings they generate. Techniques that allow regulators to compare the efficiency and effectiveness of utilities at times of price review have proved particularly helpful in establishing frontier performance. This model has operated for 20 years in the UK where it has proven sufficiently robust to enable the complete divestment of public ownership of telecom, water, waste water, electricity transmission and distribution, power generation and gas distribution and transmission assets. In these cases, substantial efficiencies have been generated and returned to customers and reinvested into these industries.

3.3.2 Rate setting

This is a regulatory process that is favoured in North America. It is highly flexible and can be applied to quite small utilities. However, this flexibility means rate-setting regulation can vary in tone and style from city to city. Large differences in methodology and application can emerge between states and provinces.

The process works by establishing the cost of running the utility for a typical base, or historic, year and adding and subtracting allowed costs to create a budget for the utility. The capital cost of improvement schemes and financing charges are agreed and these costs are then allocated to different consumer groups.

The flexibility of the process means cost-effective rate reviews can be undertaken annually for small towns or neighbourhoods, or more frequently to take account of new developments. Rate reviews are generally initiated by the utility in order to secure budgets for unexpected costs. The strong focus on historic budgets and the cost to different customer groups mean rates charged can also be low.

In addition, local political ownership of costs and benefits is very helpful and effective. However, the ad-hoc nature of these processes means comparative efficiency is difficult to establish and the rate-setting process can be heavily focused on short-term issues and outcomes. Certainly, compared with the UK, the lower levels of investment in the North American electricity transmission network, the lower rate of replacement of the cast-iron gas distribution network and the later adoption in many of the smaller utilities of basic asset management tools – such as point asset registers and Geographical Information Systems – are symptoms of a lower need for medium-term asset planning capability.

It is unlikely the greater focus on short-term outcomes in North America is a function of the rate review process itself. Indeed, there are many examples of very thoughtful and sophisticated rate review processes being conducted for the larger utility networks. Effective and objective medium-term planning is harder to achieve and less necessary because of the small size of many utilities, the different regimes applied by different states and the option managers have of seeking rate reviews at times of their choosing.

3.3.3 Regulation by concession

In this model, the ownership of utility assets can remain public, but contracts to operate and manage the utility are competitively tendered.

The nature of the services is determined by several factors: the contract length, which can vary from two to 35 years, the terms and conditions, the degree of competition for new contracts and the scope for interim reviews and appeals. This is the approach favoured in France and in the London Underground Public-Private Partnership (PPP), and adopted by much of Latin America in the late 1990s.

Frequently cited benefits of the French concession model are long-term stability, low regulatory costs and strong local accountability.

3.4 The key elements of British regulation

In the UK, price reviews establish the levels of funding, customer service outcomes and environmental and health and safety improvements that the utilities must deliver, usually for a five-year period.

Price reviews are undertaken for all utilities in a particular sector at the same time, which for water, waste water, electricity and gas distribution gives the appropriate regulators access to large volumes of comparative information. The regulatory price review process itself is complex and can take up to three years to complete. Reviews are usually held at five-year intervals, although interim reviews have been used in gas distribution, water and electricity transmission.

In simple terms, the regulated utilities agree with the regulator on the amount customers should be charged over the period of the review. They also agree the types of environmental and service improvements that must be delivered in considerable detail. This requires extensive consultation with other key stakeholders, of which the various quality regulators and customer champions are the most important.

The price review process starts with the regulator publishing the methodologies and timetable that will be used. The key processes in a regulatory review are as follows:

3.4.1 Review of prior performance against the previous regulatory contract

Historic financial and service performance is reviewed. This may involve a review to establish if investment has, with hindsight, proved efficient. Additional regulatory funding can also be allowed for material changes that have occurred which were outside the utility's control. Previously allowed funding can also be withdrawn if the objectives of the investment weren't achieved. This backward-looking review is concluded at the end of the regulatory period, while annual reviews will have already occurred. These individual reviews are critical in establishing the key facts and issues. In the water and sewerage industries, the annual reports are called 'The June Return'. In the electricity industry, the RRP (Regulatory Reporting Packs) process undertakes a similar function.

3.4.2 Measuring comparative efficiency

This process compares the operating costs on a comparative basis for each utility, thereby establishing average and frontier levels of performance. Techniques evolve continually and are challenged as different methodologies may favour different companies while regional differences and local issues may highlight special factors and allowances. Figure 3.1 illustrates the outcome from Ofgem's November 2004 review of electricity distribution companies' performance in 2002/03.

In this particular example, the vertical axis details 'NCCF', which is a composite measure of specific operational and capital costs that are driven by day-to-day operational and maintenance network activities. The horizontal axis (CSV or 'Composite Scale Variable') is a simple weighted measure of network size, driven by a series of metrics, such as the length of different types of network and the population served.

3.4.3 Unit cost challenge

The unit costs of capital works, connections and other activities are compared and contrasted to establish efficiency challenges.

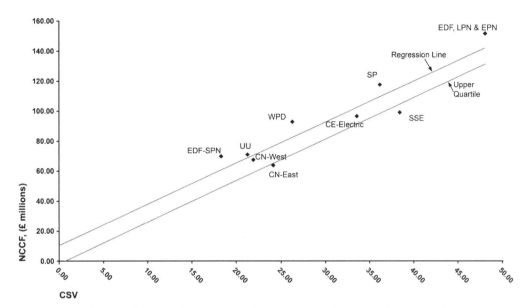

Figure 3.1 Regulatory regression analysis of the 2002/03 comparative efficiency of British electricity distribution companies

Techniques are continually challenged and improved. For illustrative purposes, Figure 3.2 shows the normalised capex cost of gas industry connections work, which was published by Ofgem at the conclusion of the Gas Distribution Price Control Review in December 2007.

3.4.4 Cost of capital: the allowable return on debt and equity used by businesses is calculated and determined. It is an important process: a high return could allow companies to make excessive profits while conversely, if the cost of capital was too low, the companies would be unable to raise the finance they require to fund their capital programmes.

3.4.5 Customer preferences: the views and requirements of customers are formally investigated by the regulated utilities and by the regulator. The sophistication of this type of work is improving with each price review. Figure 3.3 shows the results of work by United Utilities to quantify its customers' willingness to pay (or seek price reductions) for a range of new services.

Strategic Asset Management

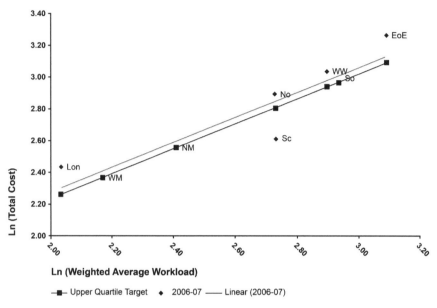

Figure 3.2 Regression of 2006/07 connections gross capex against weighted average workload (2005/06 prices).

	Current levels of service	Alternative levels of service	Average customer willingness to pay for new service level
Interruptions to supply (properties off-supply for more than six hours each year)	5,000	3,000	£8.50
External flooding from sewers (incidents each year)	3,500	1,750	£6.79
Internal flooding from sewers (properties affected each year)	1,100	550	£21.48
Odour from sewage treatment works (number of complaints each year)	1,000	500	£6.71
Greenhouse gas emissions (thousand tonnes CO_2 emissions each year)	488	462	£2.80
Security of supply (frequency of hosepipe bans in years)	20	30	£6.15
Drinking water discolouration (customer complaints each year)	22,000	12,000	£5.45
Drinking water taste and smell (customer complaints each year)	5,000	2,500	£8.11
Environmental river quality (miles of rivers in good quality each year)	2,600	2,700	£2.88
Pollution to rivers (number of serious pollution incidents each year)	15	10	£7.03
Low pressure (number of events each year)	18,000	13,000	£0
Recreational bathing water quality (% of beaches meeting guideline standard each year)	33	50	£2.55

Figure 3.3 The 'willingness to pay' of United Utilities' customers for a range of potential service improvements

3.4.6 Agreeing the size of service improvements: the economic regulator will undertake a period of challenge and consultation with quality regulators to establish the benefits of new investment to:

- Improve service (for example, to reduce risk of water shortages in periods of drought)
- Improve safety (such as the cast-iron replacement programme in the gas industry to reduce the risk of explosion)
- Improve the environment (for example, improved sewage treatment standards to improve river water quality).

3.4.7 Agreeing the scale of asset replacement/capital maintenance[2] necessary

This subject is highly contentious as asset replacement investment levels are rising. These are being driven up by a combination of factors: historic underinvestment, the increasing use of shorter-life assets (such as mechanical processes, information systems, signalling and process control systems) and the growing numbers of equipment types reaching their end-of-life simultaneously.

Determining the right scale of asset replacement investment allowed to maintain existing assets is a complex process because objective 'bottom up' projections of future funding requirements can only be derived by aggregating the impact of thousands of potential future asset failures. This creates a major challenge for regulators and the boards of utility companies, which need to agree and live with what is effectively a five-year fixed price contract to manage and maintain a complex utility system. The traditional regulatory approach has been to adjust historic levels of asset replacement funding to make allowance for the impact of new factors, such as the cumulative impact of ageing systems.

---

[2] 'Capital maintenance', 'asset replacement' and 'infrastructure renewal' are all terms used by different utility sectors and regulators to describe the investment needed to replace worn out utility equipment on a 'like for like' basis. For the purpose of this book these activities are cumulatively referred to as 'asset replacement' activities.

However, assessing the degree to which service levels should rise and differentiating between inefficient maintenance and under-funding of asset replacement is difficult. Sophisticated tools to quantify risk and demonstrate the need for future maintenance funding were first developed in the gas and electricity sectors. These approaches are now being applied to the water, waste water and rail sectors, where scale and complexity create significant additional complications. These tools and techniques are discussed further in Chapter 9.

Regulators are also recognising that asset replacement plans will be more robust if a comprehensive asset management system is used to generate them. Accordingly, in 2001 Ofgem introduced its asset risk management review (ARM), which assessed the capability of the asset management systems used by Electricity Distribution Network Operators ahead of the 2004 Regulatory Price Review. Ofwat's MD161 Letter to the water industry in April 2000 formally signalled a requirement for the industry to use 'systematic information' to produce economic projections justifying different levels of customer service attributable to different levels of asset replacement or capital maintenance investment.

In February 2006, Ofwat issued its MD212 Letter to water companies, setting out the four principles that should underpin the water industry's capital maintenance requirements at the 2009 Price Review:

1. **Forward looking:** A greater focus on forward-looking risk-based methodologies with less emphasis on historic levels of spend. An objective of this approach is to ensure companies with comparatively high maintenance allowances do not benefit indefinitely.

2. **Penalties and incentives:** In order to avoid rewarding failure, Ofwat announced a regime in which utilities that failed to maintain agreed serviceability levels would receive less funding.

3. **Capex and Opex:** A condition of funding future works is a greater focus now on ensuring all solutions used efficient mixes of capex and opex.

4. **Rigour:** A greater level of rigour is expected to underpin all funding requests. In particular, demonstrable improvements in asset data and risk-based analytical approaches, and minimised use of expert judgement.

Subsequent methodology instructions issued by Ofwat for the 2009 water and waste water price review required utilities to quantify customers' willingness to pay for proposed service levels. In addition, a requirement to apply cost benefit analysis to factors such as carbon accounting, noise, land usage, odour, and customer interruptions of supply when proposing programmes of work was introduced.

In conjunction with the 2009 Electricity Distribution Price Review, Ofgem now requires step changes in the quantification of asset risk modelling to ensure asset replacement and reinforcement plans are effective and good value. The implications of these regulatory requirements on the capabilities of the asset management systems are discussed in Chapter 6.

3.5 Regulatory tensions and challenges

The economic regulator has a role in determining the utilities' service standards and investment objectives and their level of charges. Other regulators, such as the British Environment Agencies, have a duty to protect the environment and implement legislation. The differing objectives of such regulators can cause tensions that are not easy to resolve. For example, European directives – such as the Urban Waste Water Treatment Directive (UWWTD), the Bathing Water Directive, the Shellfish Directive and the Ground Water Directive – can be highly beneficial but extremely complex to implement.

Frequently, legislation is a mixture of prescriptive responses and locally designated improvement objectives. For example, the objective of the UWWTD and the Shell Fish Directive is to protect the European environment from the adverse effects of sewage discharges. It does so by setting discharge conditions with due regard to the impact of sewage discharges and the sensitivity of receiving waters. Environmental regulators have a role to play in establishing the sensitivity of particular river or esturine waters, or in the designation of specific areas of shellfish. These decisions can trigger the need for large investments that must be funded through water bills. The complexity of many of these local decisions and their cumulative effect makes the economic regulators' task of satisfying itself that bills are affordable and good value a challenge.

Large investment projects can also create other policy and environmental conflicts. The carbon footprint of an effective new sewage treatment works may do more damage over time through greenhouse emissions than the removal of low levels of pollutants is an ecological benefit to river water quality.

There are many examples of new quality initiatives creating complex policy conflicts and unwelcome new costs for utility customers. For example, the Habitats Directive makes the abstraction of water from reservoirs and rivers more difficult in summer months because it causes stress in the wildlife that have colonised the reservoir. Close co-operation between regulators and utilities and the sharing of information are essential if these complex trade-offs are to be effectively resolved in the long-term interest of all stakeholders. Many of the tools used to do so are described in Chapter 9.

3.6 Regulatory outcomes and experiences

The French concession approach – ownership of water utility assets by the local municipality – has many interesting and attractive facets that make it a simple and responsive solution: the long-term stability of the regime, the low regulatory costs, the high reliance on competitive pressures and the close relationship between the 30,000 water distribution and sewage service areas[3] and the local service provider.

[3] Competition and Economic Regulation in Water Tony Ballance and Andrew Taylor, IWA Publishing.

In contrast, however, the lack of information on comparative costs, the fact that a handful of very large private businesses win all concessions and that few, if any, non-French companies have done so raises several issues. It may be that the French model is highly appropriate to a large, lightly populated country and the practice of companies close to the French state of sharing a small pool of executive skills provides a powerful restraint to a potential abuse of monopoly power[4]. However, the partial withdrawal of French companies from early ownership of British privatised utilities, in response to reported low returns from the activity, makes this issue opaque.

The outcomes for Latin America appear, at first glance, highly satisfactory. By the end of the 1990s, investment flows of US$360m had been generated and there was evidence of efficiency gains of 2% per annum in contracted services at a time when no similar efficiencies were evident in public corporations[5]. Much higher efficiency gains were observed for railway concessions in Argentina and Brazil[6]. However, regulatory weaknesses meant these substantial efficiency gains were captured by the state in the form of taxes[7]. In addition, while the investment levels are impressive, they only represented a third of the funding required by the industry[8] and investment was often focused on high-profile prestige projects and

[4] Shugart, C Regulation by Contract and municipal Services, PhD Thesis, Harvard University, Cambridge, Massachusetts, 1998.

[5] Production Frontier Analysis: Electricity Distribution Sector in South America, MPhil thesis, University of Oxford,: Rossi M (200)] [Rossi M (2001) Technical Challenge and Efficiency Measures: The Post-Privatisation in the Gas Distribution Sector of Argentina, Energy Economics 23 (3), 295-304: Rossi M (2002),

[6] Estache A, Gonzalez M and Trujillo L (2002a) What does Privatization do for Efficiency? Evidence from Argentina's and Brazil's Railways, World Development, Vol. 30, No11, November.

[7] Price Caps, Efficiency Pay-offs and Infrastructure Contract Renegotiation in Latin America, Antonio Estache, Jose-Luis Guasch and Lourdes Trujillo, Proceedings of 'The UK Model of Utility Regulation, 9th April 2003, The University of Bath, ISBN 1 85790 119 3.

[8] Fay M (2000), The Infrastructure Needs of Latin America, The World Bank, the annual investments needed for 2000-2005.

Industry sector	Compound real operating efficiency (%)
Water	3.7
Sewerage	4.1
Electricity transmission	6.5
Electricity distribution	6.8
Gas	9.1

Figure 3.4 Post-privatisation annual efficiency gains in the UK

regions. The governments were then left with the obligations to fund the service needs of higher-risk, lower cash-flow regions[9].

Privatisation and regulation of the water, electricity and gas industries in the UK have proved to be contentious but highly successful. Not only did those businesses fund in excess of £100bn of new investment in the 20 years following privatisation, but the quality of service and health and safety improved, and real compound operating efficiencies (detailed below in Figure 3.4[10]) were delivered.

Benefits to the English and Welsh water and waste water industries include[11]:

- Leakage levels 35% lower than they were in the mid-1990s
- Improved water company compliance with environmental standards
- £80bn of funding secured from the financial markets to fund environmental improvements

9 Price Caps, Efficiency Pay-offs and Infrastructure Contract Renegotiation in Latin America, Antonio Estache, Jose-Luis Guasch and Lourdes Trujillo, Proceedings of 'The UK Model of Utility Regulation, 9th April 2003, The University of Bath, ISBN 1 85790 119 3.
[10] European Economics, "Review of Railtrack Efficiency", 9 December 1999, p15
[11] Ofwat's response to the Cave Review's final report on competition and Innovation in Water Markets [in England and Wales].
http://www.ofwat.gov.uk/competition/res_ofw_cavereport.pdf

- Water bills that are now 30% lower than they would have been if privitisation and regulation had not been introduced.

Notwithstanding these improvements, the actual cost to households of water bills has risen 42%, and customers are demanding better service and value.

However, the introduction of effective regulation is a complex process, and other regions have seen failures of regulation and markets. The Californian Electricity Crisis of 2000 and 2001 is a case in point. A combination of unsustainable price controls and market imperfections meant power companies could not recover the costs of generating electricity from their customers. This resulted in the bankruptcy of Pacific Gas and Electric and the public bailout of Enron and Reliant Energy. Customers experienced many months of power cuts followed by the declaration of a state of emergency, which lasted until November 2003.

3.7 The importance of other unregulated factors

In the absence of a competitive market, economic regulators seek to determine the appropriate level of funding and the right service standards that a utility should deliver. It is then the role of utility managers and leaders to establish corporate objectives and an appropriate asset management system.

In practice, there are significant events that many utilities experience at some point in a regulatory cycle over which economic regulators and managers have little control. Clearly the advent of negative inflation and the near-collapse of the global financial markets in 2009 were unforeseen and exceptional events that affected all of us. However, there are many more commonplace examples, any one of which utility management may find it needs to address, including:

- Enormous unserviceable demand for new services in or out of region/country leading to supply-chain failure.

- The appointment of corporate administrators and/or change in ownership.
- Changes in interpretation of health and safety or environmental legislation following a court ruling.
- Continual involvement of local or national politicians in management issues.
- Significant difficulty of getting access to land/land rights.

In addition, in the absence of a truly independent economic regulator the annual revision of budgets by local or central government or an organisation's corporate function can make the role of managers and the operation of an asset management system extremely difficult. Utilities, unlike many traditional businesses, cannot be allowed to fail and cease trading, as failure of utility services typically leads to broad economic paralysis and, quite quickly, civil disruption.

When a utility's strategic asset management system is operated by groups far removed from the day-to-day management, the objective and rational quantification of utility risk and service is important to help, and hold to account, those parties. For these reasons, the management of utility funding, risk and service occurs through a complex continuum of economic regulation, tough leadership, political insight and management of public expectation. In reality, the mix and relevance of all these factors changes from time to time and from utility sector to sector.

The public and political perception of utilities is also an important factor in influencing the outcome of regulatory reviews and rate setting processes.

Case study 1: Wall Street Journal 21 February 2009 (by Christopher Conkey).

The chief executive of Amtrack said Americans should expect only "incremental" progress in improving passenger rail service, despite an $8 billion program. [..] Amtrack stands to receive nearly

$3 billion this year, more than double its usual funding level. But CEO Joseph Boardman said in an interview that previous shortages, a backlog of deferred maintenance and last year's record ridership[12] have produced a government-owned rail corporation being held together "with chewing gum and rubber bands".

[..] The amount of money provided in the stimulus package for transportation projects and the requirement to spend it quickly means the emphasis will be on small-scale rehabilitation work rather than new roads, tunnels or transit systems. [..] Mr. Boardman's view was echoed Wednesday (sic) by other government officials. John Smith, mayor of Meridian, Miss., said the high-speed-rail funding would go into "incremental projects which will improve trip times on existing routes".

[12] Passenger Volumes

Case study 2: The impact of privatisation on utility reputation and the relationship with the public
On this subject one highly experienced senior utility manager commented:

"It can get very difficult sometimes. When we ran the network as a [government-owned corporation] failure was seen as occasional incompetence, and while not acceptable it was inevitable or understandable. Now when something goes wrong the presumption seems to be we have caused the problem by stealing from customers to grow profits."

The cumulative impact of many of these issues and their potential impact on determining the types of asset management systems that are appropriate for a particular utility will be explored in more detail in Chapter 6.

3.8 Conclusions

The key points are as follows:

- Effective regulation ensures that utilities themselves become more efficient and that these benefits are passed to consumers, while weak regulation can result in excess profits for utilities, and poor customer and environmental service.
- Regulators must be independent of government if the capital markets are to have confidence in the regulatory regime and any efficiency gains are not captured by the state.
- There are two types of economic regulation (Incentive-Based Price Setting and Rate Setting) and one type of competitive form (Concession) of price setting.
- Co-operation between different types of regulators is necessary, as is recognition by economic regulators that utility managers may face pressures from factors outside its control and influence.
- Care must also be taken to ensure the whole cost which the complexity and degree of intrusion associated with a particular regulatory process reflects value for money for customers.

The growth of regulatory pressures is a significant factor in determining the nature and rigour that a utility's asset management system must provide. This issue is explored further in Chapter 6.

Further reading

Competition and Economic Regulation in Water, Tony Ballance and Andrew Taylor.
The UK Model of Utility Regulation, A 20th anniversary collection to make the 'Littlechild Report'-retrospect and prospect. (London Business School, City University, CRI, University of Bath School of Management.)

4 The Scale of Modern Utilities

4.0 Introduction

The challenge for modern utility asset managers, regulators and suppliers is to optimise customer service and value by balancing performance, cost and risk. This may sound a simple task; however the geographical scale of these businesses, the very large number of different types of assets and their complex interactions as a system makes this extremely difficult to do in practice. Under stable conditions, several years can pass with almost all of a utility's assets continually used and yet, during that time, by value, only a tiny percentage is maintained or replaced. At the same time, there is a possibility any of them might fail, affecting service or stopping it altogether.

This chapter reviews the relative scales of modern network utilities and seeks to show the relative size of operating and capital investing activities within utilities. The scale and nature of these functions are important in determining where organisational power and influence can exist and the degree of complexity that a utility's asset management system must control.

Figures and information from different cost bases and, indeed, different accounting assumptions (between regulators, industries and companies) have been reviewed. The figures, however, are more than accurate enough to give an understanding of the relative importance of investing and operating challenges within different utility industries.

These figures are particularly relevant to the UK, although other regions are mirroring the UK's experience or are likely to do so in the medium term. Accordingly, the UK experience is relevant to the challenges utility operators, suppliers and regulators are experiencing in many parts of the world.

4.1 Modern utility assets

In any populated region of the world, utility networks run under every street, across cities and the countryside. Although they were most likely the first infrastructure that was established when the village, town or city was founded, they are often invisible. Since then, they will have been expanding and developing year by year, either due to new connections or a need for improved quality or safety.

4.2 Utility services in the north west of England

The North West of England has many features common to the mature utility networks in mixed urban and rural regions of Europe and North America. The region is home to 6.9[1] million people and approximately 3.1 million households. It contains mature and growing cities, such as Liverpool and Manchester, a large industrial heritage and extensive unpopulated national parks, such as the Lake District and the Peak District.

The estimated replacement costs of the utility networks in the North West of England are detailed below in Figure 4.1.

This means that, on average, the replacement value for every household's gas, water, sewage and electricity services is in the order of £28,000. This figure would be much greater if the assets needed to find and extract gas, generate electricity and provide transport services, such as highways and railways, were taken into account.

4.2.1 Water collection, treatment and supply

There are more than 42,000km of water mains and aqueducts serving

---

[1] Office of National Statistics (2007).

Utility Sector	Utility Infrastructure Replacement Value £ (bn)	Percentage %
Sewage drainage	31	35%
Sewage treatment	6	7%
Sewage total	**37**	**42%**
Electricity distribution	**13**	**15%**
Water distribution	15	17%
Water treatment	4	5%
Water total	**19**	**22%**
Gas distribution	**4.8**	**5%**
Gas & electricity transmission	**14**	**16%**
TOTALS	**88**	**100%**

Figure 4.1 Replacement Costs for Utility Asset Bases in the North West Region of England

the region. Water mains vary from several centimetres to more than a metre in diameter and operate at such high pressures that if a major main fractures, the force of the escaping water could lift up and carry a road surface away in minutes. Some of the longest rivers in the North West of England, in fact, are the underground aqueducts that supply Manchester and Liverpool with water from the Lake District and Wales. These aqueducts travel many hundreds of kilometres across valleys and through hills. The internal diameter of these assets can be as great as 3.5 metres and at times they are located at depths of up to 350 metres below ground.

There are also 95 water treatment works that draw water from 189 impounding reservoirs, boreholes and rivers. Treatment works can vary in size from small warehouses to enormous structures covering many hundreds of hectares. There are 608 pumping stations and 449 service reservoirs, which fill up during the night and hold water ready for use by customers the following day.

Water treatment and distribution networks must respond to and address rigorous compliance measures. Numerous meters, chlorination injection processes, and pressure and flow valves split the network into discrete zones and areas, all of which can be separately managed and controlled. As water disinfection is critical the regular sampling, inspection and reporting of critical chemical and bacteriological measures ensure a tight control over all treatment processes is maintained. Water filtering and treatment processes, which operate continuously, require extensive instrumentation and data reporting systems. Improvements in water treatment processes in conjunction with the cleaning and refurbishing of the down stream networks can be necessary to deliver water quality improvements to a range of different measures, such as trace metals content and water colour and turbidity improvements. But it is often difficult to directly link investment to performance benefits, which makes investment management difficult.

An audit trail is essential. Every operational manager's greatest fear is that a process fails for some hours, a critical issue develops, and a boil water order must be issued to all affected households.

Leakage reporting and control is a very public and high-profile measure, which creates a demanding environment in which 24/7 leakage reporting, detection and resolution are necessary to achieve annual leakage targets.

4.2.2   Waste water collection and treatment

In the North West of England there are 44,000km of gravity, or pumped, sewers. Sewers vary in size from small clay pipes to brick tunnels that are large enough to accommodate a fire engine, with nearly half a million manhole covers and inspection points. The stock of manhole covers alone is worth £50 million.

The drainage network uses 1,800 underground pumping stations, some the size of a small garage, others enormous sprawling structures built into the bedrock beneath the streets. Some 3,600 other structures – such as storage tanks and equipment that screens waste water to remove litter and debris – can also be found along the network.

Treatment is undertaken at 582 waste water treatment works and 61 sewage sludge treatment centres. These treatment plants can be small plants treating the sewage coming from a small village, or large plants covering hundreds of acres with storm tanks as big as ships and surrounded by perimeter fences many kilometres in length.

Most modern and comprehensive drainage networks will drain rainwater and sewage effectively for 99.9% of the year, while foul flooding is on average a one-in-a-thousand year event. However a small proportion of properties are particularly vulnerable to flooding and to seek to control these events asset managers must address the following issues:

- Create hydraulic models and use them for planning all work, taking into account seasonal variations and climatic change
- Identify and remove silting up of sewers and tree root ingress
- Plan for and support the progressive introduction of new approaches, such as 'sustainable urban drainage'[2]
- Enforce trade effluent controls to ensure fatty wastes do not accumulate in sewers and cause blockages
- Inspect and repair the fabric of sewers to ensure collapses do not occur
- Work with planning authorities to help control new load growth as developers connect new properties to the network.

Working with and in sewers can be challenging and unpleasant. The threat of hypodermic needles and the presence of toxic or explosive gases are ever-present. Almost anything you care to think of has been found in a sewer, from drugs and rats to false teeth and mattresses.

Treatment of waste water is now a complex process. Initial grit and litter removal is followed by an extensive treatment process that includes the following:

[2] Introduce porous driveways, replace tarmac with grass and other measures which allow rain water to drain naturally and not be collected by the sewer systems.

- Primary settlement to separate primary sludge and liquid effluent.
- Secondary treatment to biologically remove pollutants from the liquid effluent.
- Further settlement to create secondary sludges and an even cleaner effluent.
- Tertiary biological treatment of this effluent to remove more trace pollutants, such as ammonia or phosphorous.
- Ultraviolet and, occasionally, chemical disinfection of liquid effluent to remove trace pathogens.
- Collection of sludge volumes, dewatering and pumping or transport to centralised treatment centres.
- Anaerobic digestion of sludge (frequently in conjunction with biogas generation and power generation).
- Dewatering of digested sludge, and its subsequent composting, drying and or usage as a fertiliser or as a fuel source in incineration.

All these processes operate all day, all night, all year and rely on substantial vehicle tanker operations and complex instrumentation and control systems.

4.2.3   Electricity Distribution

The North West Electricity Distribution network is built from more than:

- 17,000km of overhead lines
- 59,000km of underground cable
- 140,000 items of switchgear
- 46,000 transformers
- 25,000 substations.

This network is managed and operated in real time, and employs sophisticated automatic control systems to protect it from damage when events cause short-circuiting. If these measures were not taken, the amount of energy in a utility network could result in it damaging itself during localised failure.

In addition to operating the system, an electricity utility has to inspect and maintain its thousands of substations. This is necessary to make it difficult for people to force entry to these assets, which are almost always located in highly populated areas. Although substations can be dangerous places, some people, including children, are still prepared to go to exceptional lengths to gain entry.

General maintenance of overhead lines and tree cutting and trimming are essential to make the power supply as resilient as possible in times of storm. Inspection and general maintenance of switchgear are also critical to prolonging the life of these assets. As switchgear contains large volumes of insulating oil, the failure of these items can result in explosion and the violent escape of oil. A great many techniques, working methods and special instrumentation have been developed to prevent, anticipate and detect possible equipment failures. Fault repair is a major activity. Regulatory incentives and penalties that are directly linked to those periods when customers are off-supply mean capital work and planned maintenance are frequently at risk of disruption from rising fault levels or major incidents. In storm conditions, the overhead network can suffer enormous damage. At such times the safe restoration of services is the priority and all other work is sidelined.

4.2.4 Gas Distribution

The gas network in the North West of England is composed of approximately 50 gas holders, 1,000km of high pressure gas mains and a further 34,000km of intermediate, medium and low pressure gas mains.

The explosive nature of gas means safety is a critical issue for the gas industry. This presents major challenges for the managers and supervisors, who frequently must make complex engineering decisions to allow efficient operation and maintenance of the network while taking the necessary steps to address health and safely issues. Not only does that require safe systems of work but it also demands that a large programme to replace old iron pipes with polyethylene plastic pipes becomes a national priority.

There are plans, for example, to replace approximately 100,000km, which comprises 50% of the UK network, by 2032. In the North West of England the cost of this programme and other capital maintenance is approximately £115m per annum. Efficient 'street working' must be a key focus if these projects are to be delivered quickly and safely with minimum disturbance. A complex process for prioritising cast-iron main replacement is already in place. The following factors are used to estimate the asset risk and prioritise gas main replacement work:

- Pipe construction material
- Asset type
- Ground conditions
- Jointing type
- Proximity to buildings
- Type of buildings
- Pressure of main.

Planning such schemes and scheduling replacement and liaising with members of the public are also priorities. As the methodology for prioritising and programming the cast-iron mains replacement programme makes up the majority of the investment, with few other major asset management decisions, the role of the asset manager is relatively non-contentious in the gas industry. However, the risk of gas escapes and any subsequent gas explosion demands heavy supervision and compliance for all operational and construction elements. In the event of an incident, every operational decision, method of work, engineering drawing and pipe weld will likely be inspected to establish the root cause. As a consequence, the gas industry has developed some of the most complex day-to-day asset risk management approaches in the utility sector.

A major task for the staff managing a gas network is to respond at all hours to calls from people who believe they can smell gas. And maintenance of above-ground assets – such as gas holders, and governors (pressure control systems) – remains essential.

4.3 Investment into utility networks

It is estimated that utilities represent more than 5% of the Gross Domestic Product of most countries. In simple terms, this means that more than a twentieth of the wealth of the entire planet is invested in the utility services we often take for granted.

In young and growing countries, the construction of new utility services is an enormous challenge but one that must be undertaken in order to enable economic growth to occur. As it takes longer to design and build utility services than it takes to build the houses and offices they serve, it is extremely difficult to build utility services efficiently in periods of high economic growth. In growing economies where this is recognised, the utility services are often high-prestige industries. In Saudi Arabia, Riyadh has grown 20-fold in size since 1980, putting immense strain on utility services and water resources, which sometimes must draw on irreplaceable fossil water[3] aquifers.

Meanwhile, in rural areas and smaller cities, a significant percentage of the population relies either on intermittent supplies of water through the distribution system or on an expensive water supply from water trucks. In the United Arab Emirates, where economic and population growth has been occurring at 5% to 15% per annum for many years, the planned provision of utility services is a priority. Notably, Abu Dhabi has established an Abu Dhabi Urban Planning Council which has the powers to co-ordinate and sponsor long-term planning. To this end, an Urban Plan for the City of Abu Dhabi was published in 2007 for the period until 2030. This is a rare and visionary commitment to address and fund a variety of aspects of urban development and infrastructure so the city can achieve its

---

[3] Fossil water aquifers are ancient underground water reserves which are unlikely to be replenished naturally.

goal of being a prosperous and pleasant place in which to live.

Throughout Europe and North America, high levels of investment in utility infrastructure are necessary but for different reasons. In these regions, the existing infrastructure is old and fast approaching the point when replacement is becoming increasingly critical. In addition, the need to retrofit safer and more environmentally effective processes is proving complex and expensive. As many of the new infrastructure systems use sophisticated control systems and instrumentation, which need careful management and frequent replacement, the industry is transforming into a much more complex one than it was 50 years ago.

By way of example, the typical investment levels per household in parts of the UK are detailed in Figure 4.2 The operating costs for utility types are as shown in Figure 4.3

Household bills are not the sum of operating and investment costs. There are many other factors that should be taken into account. Indeed, the utilities have a need to finance the investment they make as they only recover the cost of investment from customers over the life of the utility assets that have been built. For households in England and Wales the make-up of utility bills is shown in Figure 4.4.

Utility	Investment p.a. (£ per property) [1]
Water treatment & distribution	£78
Wastewater treatment & Distribution	£90
Electricity distribution	£67
Gas Distribution	£37
Total	**£272**

[1] *Ofwat and Ofgem final determinations, 5 year aggregates indexed to 2007/8 cost base.*

Figure 4.2 Investment Levels per Household by Utility networks in England and Wales

Utility	Operating cost p.a. (£ per property) [2]
Water treatment & distribution	£70
Wastewater treatment & distribution	£58
Electricity distribution	£29[3]
Gas distribution	£23[4]
Total	**£180**

[2] *Ofwat and Ofgem final determinations*

[3] *Assuming 29 million households in England and Wales*

[4] *Ofgem Presentation 3 December 2007: DG Price Review Final Proposals*

Figure 4.3 Indicative Operating Costs for Different Utility Services

Utility service	2007 bills
Water collection, treatment & distribution	£129
Wastewater collection & treatment	£144
Electricity distribution & transmission[5]	£78
Electricity generation, meters, VAT (sales tax) & renewables obligation	£299
Gas distribution & transmission[6]	£125
Gas purchase, VAT (sales tax), renewables obligation & meters	£444
Total	**£1,219**

[5] *Ofgem 'Household Energy Bills', Sheet 66, 15/1/8*

[6] *Ofgem 'Household Energy Bills', Sheet 66, 15/1/8*

Figure 4.4 Domestic English and Welsh Utility Bills in 2007

Excluding the cost of generating electricity and buying gas, metering and sales taxes, the bill during the period 2006-2007 per household for gas, water, sewage and electricity transmission, distribution and drainage is about £500 per annum. More than half of these costs relate to construction works needed to replace old assets or improve the quality, environmental performance or safety of the network. Only a third of the cost now relates to the day-to-day operation.

Included within the figure for capital investment is an allowance for the replacement of existing assets, either because they have failed and need fixing or are likely to do so in the near future. In the North West of England, the amount spent on these sorts of activities is currently around £420 million per annum. At first sight, this might seem to be a great deal of money and it is therefore tempting to presume all utilities ought to be in excellent condition. However, given the total replacement value of the North West of England's asset base was earlier seen to be worth £87 billion, it follows that at this level of investment the utility assets in the North West of England must, on average, last over two centuries before they can be replaced, if this level of funding is to be sustainable. Clearly, some types of asset – such as computers, vehicles and instrumentation – must be replaced every five or 10 years, while other assets may have to last for 300 to 400 years. The North West of England is not particularly unusual in this respect. It is true that here, where the Industrial Revolution began, the situation is particularly aggravated due to the age of much of the infrastructure. However, regulators across the world have cautiously recognised the growing risk posed by ageing utility infrastructure in recent price reviews, and allowed growing levels of funding as this extract from the Binnie Report[4] makes clear:

"*Current allowance for replacement of sewers would produce lives of the order of 500 years to 1,200 years.*

[4] Future Water and Sewerage Charges 2000 – 2005 Draft Determinations, The Implications for Capital Maintenance Expenditure [in England and Wales], report by Professor Chris Binnie for Water UK, October 1999

Funding available does little more than allow for repair of sewer collapses."

However, throughout Europe and North America where the infrastructure asset base is ageing, much greater levels of funding are necessary – an unpopular and unwelcome prospect for regulators, and for customers.

4.4 Utility risk management

Utility staff are generally extremely risk adverse by nature. In part, this is a consequence of the engineering culture so prevalent in the industry. This risk-adverse culture can be highly frustrating for companies seeking to sell new products and it presents a major challenge for leadership teams seeking to encourage the right levels of ambition, value for money and ways of working.

However, it is also important the utility industries do behave and operate in a resilient and cautious manner. Utilities are typically taken for granted until such time as they (occasionally) fail. The failure of power systems or flooding defences, interruptions to transport systems, or the loss of gas pressure or water supply can result in enormous losses of industrial productivity, which in a week typically can dwarf the annual running costs of the entire utility.

Furthermore, if failure of a utility network does occur, the recovery of utility services can be extremely difficult to effect. For example:

* Loss of pressure in a gas network means subsequent re-pressurisation could allow gas to enter properties through gas appliances which have been left turned on, leading to a risk of explosion. Accordingly, it is necessary for individual properties to be inspected before re-supply with gas is possible.
* Interruptions to railway systems leave rolling stock and signalling systems in irregular locations or settings, making recovery challenging.

- Failure of water treatment processes can lead to contamination of the water supply. It may take several days for contaminants to be flushed from the network.
- If generation plant must be disconnected from the network and interconnected transmission networks lose supply, a point is reached when a 'black start' of the network is needed. It is not always evident how such events can best be undertaken.
- Loss of water pressure to a distribution network and associated flooding can result in the risk of infiltration of contaminated waters into the potable system.
- Sustained loss of power can result in inoperable security systems and lost mobile phone coverage.

For all these reasons and many more, a cautious and risk-adverse culture in the utility sector is advisable.

4.5 Conclusion

The scale of even moderately complex utilities is far beyond the imagination of any one individual. The wide range of different types of assets managed and the large numbers of interventions available to asset managers will have fundamental implications for the necessary sophistication of a utility's asset management system.

In modern times, individual operational staff have accumulated a wealth of information about the assets they operate in their neighbourhood, an invaluable body of knowledge which is needed to prioritise maintenance, investment and operational tasks in that area. However, when that person retires, much of that information is lost.

Reliance on local knowledge creates two other problems. Firstly, it is difficult for managers and regulators to establish the most urgent priorities for investment across the whole utility. Secondly, developing trends are much harder to identify. For example, it is difficult for operational managers unfamiliar with a particular area to track the changing use of road salt on the safe life of electrical pillars close to highways, or to note the risk of damage to old transformer cores caused by vibrations from pile driving in the immediate neighbourhood.

The following chapters explore how increasing pressures on modern utilities require utility sectors to establish much more effective asset management systems to manage their growing complexity. We shall also be exploring how they are responding to these challenges.

5 Asset Management Capabilities

5.0 Introduction

In the previous chapters, we explored the history and scale of utilities, and the nature of modern regulation. Hopefully, these will have provided readers with an understanding of:

- The historical utility legacy which must be managed.
- The regulatory pressures which seek to mimic competitive forces.
- The similarities and differences between the water, waste water, gas and electricity utility sectors and an appreciation of their nature.

All utilities share a scale and complexity that go beyond the knowledge and imagination of any one person. These factors, however, are sometimes not appreciated by people unfamiliar with utilities or those who have worked in other areas and are focused on delivering their own particular part of the utility service.

The complexity of utilities and their geographical nature mean local knowledge is also very important. But despite being a valuable resource that must be harnessed and protected, local knowledge can, counter-intuitively, also make the organisation and co-ordination of utilities more difficult.

Asset management systems are deployed in different ways in different geographies and utility sectors. In this chapter, the Asset Management Capability Model is introduced. This model is used throughout the remainder of the book to explain why different utilities need to adopt different approaches when they are designing and enhancing their own asset management systems. The six factors within the Asset Management Capability Model are each reviewed in the next six chapters of the book.

5.1 The emerging need for modern Asset Management systems

As was noted in Chapter 2, the term 'Asset Management' only started to be used in the utility and infrastructure sector some 30 years ago when people sought to understand the real whole cost of providing water and waste water services in South Australia.

In the following years, Asset Management thinking challenged accounting methodologies and broadened its scope to explore the accounting and funding of most Australian infrastructure, including schools, highways and utilities. Throughout the 1980's and 1990's, a range of new, disparate ideas helped lay the foundations of what we now think of as 'Asset Management'. These ideas – the application of asset condition to calculate inventory values and predict future service life, better operational control and scheduling, and development and allocation of Geographical Information Systems – have given utility managers more control and information about their businesses.

In the last 15 years, the application of Asset Management principles has focused on developing techniques and approaches that work together to enable utility and infrastructure organisations to 'see' the value in everything they do. It also helps to provide effective services to utility and infrastructure customers by balancing short and long cycle operating and investment and risk management pressures.

Most of the important asset management implementations have occurred in the last 10 years. In that sense, 'Asset Management' might appear to be a new activity for a utility sector that had managed for 150 years without it. In practice, modern asset management systems are seeking to formalise the day-to-day value judgements utility managers were making a century ago. As it was then, the challenge remains to ensure assets are built, operated, maintained and eventually decommissioned in a way that gives customers good value and service. However, the question remains: why is 'Asset Management' such a focus for operational and engineering staff in utilities today?

Many, but not all, utilities find themselves in subtly but significantly different circumstances these days. Firstly, modern utilities are now much more complex than ever before and this makes the challenges of balancing opex and capex costs and assessing asset risk much more difficult. This situation is aggravated by the growing numbers of utility infrastructure assets which are reaching the end of their lives. Managing equipment efficiently and effectively and delaying high equipment replacement costs also remain important issues.

Secondly, health and safety and environmental standards are much higher. In Chapter 2 we saw that the working life of an operative working in the coking ovens in London in the 1840's was less than eight years. These days, cast-iron gas pipes are being replaced to reduce the risk to the public of explosions at an estimated cost of £100m-£200m per life saved. In the waste water sector, it was not unusual 20 years ago for large coastal sewage treatment plants to make use of only primary settlement to treat raw sewage; however, secondary and tertiary treatment, sometimes with UV disinfection, are increasingly being retrofitted to sewage treatment plants. In some cases new treatment standards require the entire treatment plant to be rebuilt and modernised.

Although many utilities see the development of their asset management systems as a strategic priority, many others feel there is less opportunity or value in adopting the leading approaches. There are big differences in the degree of sophistication of asset management systems – between different utility industries and even within utility sectors. The appetite and the approach to improving the capability of asset management systems will vary from utility to utility. At first sight, these apparent differences seem unusual. Clearly, different leaders will have different visions for their particular utilities. However, the implementation of new aspects of an asset management system carries risk, and a bad or inappropriate asset management system can destroy value and slow down decision-making.

In deciding the type of asset management system that is efficient and effective for a particular utility, it is helpful to break down the complexity of the options and pressures a utility faces into separate elements. For utilities, there are several considerations that determine how the asset management system will operate and its capability:

*   The **climate** a utility operates in.
*   The internal **complexity** of the utility.
*   The organisation's **goals**.
*   The asset management **tools**.
*   The design of the **organisation**.
*   **Teams** and team working.

These six factors define the asset management capability an infrastructure company needs and is able to implement. The character and relationship between these six factors is illustrated in the asset management capability model, which is discussed below. This capability model is used throughout the rest of the book to illustrate the choices, techniques and pressures different utilities have made and experienced on their own efficiency and improvement journeys.

5.2 The asset management capability model

We can take a view on a utility's current asset management capability by undertaking PAS 55 audits and talking to staff. This observed 'capability' results from the cumulative impact of the six factors within the capability model shown in Figure 5.1

No particular mix of the factors within the capability model creates a preferred asset management system for a particular utility. For example, there is no particular organisational structure that is

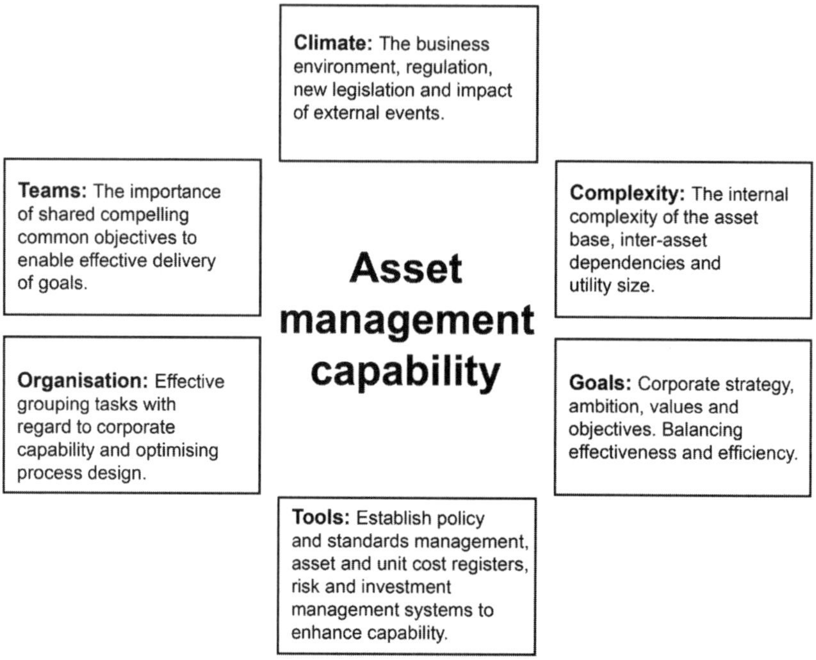

Climate: The business environment, regulation, new legislation and impact of external events.

Teams: The importance of shared compelling common objectives to enable effective delivery of goals.

Asset management capability

Complexity: The internal complexity of the asset base, inter-asset dependencies and utility size.

Organisation: Effective grouping tasks with regard to corporate capability and optimising process design.

Goals: Corporate strategy, ambition, values and objectives. Balancing effectiveness and efficiency.

Tools: Establish policy and standards management, asset and unit cost registers, risk and investment management systems to enhance capability.

Figure 5.1 Asset Management Capability Model

'best', sub-contracting out or in can both be valid strategies and if the climate in which a utility operates is benign, there may be less need for a formal asset management system. However, if there is a mismatch between any of the six factors outlined above, then the capability and effectiveness of the asset management system may be inappropriate. The next six chapters examine each of the factors within the model, while case studies illustrate the issues and choices that can arise.

5.3 The importance of information

In order to see the links between the six elements of the capability model and the ways in which they interact, it is helpful to consider a utility's requirements for information and data.

As we seek to deliver value and service, a key challenge for all organisations is to collect and process relevant information and data.

Trading, for example, requires that market share information, sales forecasts, production plans, budget preparation and cash collection information and data be collected and managed. The physical element of doing business – such as fabricating and dispatching products, operating bank branches or fixing a broken pump – is clearly crucial but in itself, cannot define how the organisation should be organised and represents only one part in the added value of the business.

Accordingly, information – which highlights what needs to be done, when and by whom – and maintaining and sustaining the businesses are central to defining how the business can exist and prosper. The asset management systems that utilities operate, in other words, are essentially their data and information planning systems. For utilities, these systems can be extremely complex but most elements of a utility's asset management system are also used, sometimes in an informal manner, by other types of organisations that operate and maintain physical assets.

In 1974, in his defining paper 'Organisational Design: An information Processing View'[1], Professor JR Galbraith explained that the way an organisation handles information was a key principle which determined realistic options for business strategies and organisational design. Professor Galbraith proposed that management, as a consequence, has three different strategies to ensure appropriate responses to the challenges and opportunities of handling corporate information. These are:

Strategy 1: Be better at planning so work can be organised and scheduled. This requires a business to invest in information systems, tools and communication techniques. Larger utilities, for example, are investing heavily in Asset Registers, ERP systems,[2] Geographical Information Systems, investment prioritisation systems and many of the tools and processes discussed in Chapter 9.

[1] Interfaces Volume 4, No 3 May 1974 copyright ©1974 The Institute of Management Sciences.
[2] Enterprise Resource Planning systems. A term used to refer to major corporate work and material management systems.

Strategy 2: Where planning is unable to anticipate events, the organisation needs to be sufficiently flexible to accommodate urgent late requirements. For utilities, this can be achieved by adopting organisational designs with self-contained decision-making groups that have sufficient resources (funding and/or delivery capability) and the authority to manage issues as they arise. Traditionally, utilities have found organisational structures that devolve budgets to managers of geographical areas an effective solution. Where other, more preferable, options exist, this approach can be an effective and resilient strategy but inefficient. Yet it remains a practical solution, or part solution, for utilities such as nuclear processing processes or waste water treatment businesses. The organisational options utilities may consider are discussed further in Chapter 10.

Strategy 3: Accept that a reduction in service quality or efficiency is necessary and take appropriate steps to ensure this solution is acceptable to stakeholders, such as regulators or customers.

Case Study 1: UK gas industry iron main replacement programme

In common with many of the mature economies, the UK's gas distribution network was laid up to 150 years ago. In time, these materials have become increasingly vulnerable to ground and traffic movements. The growing risk of the pipe wall being fractured, gas escaping, leading to its accumulation in buildings and a subsequent explosion means these issues need to be treated with the greatest care.

Considerable work during the 1970s and 1980s focused on gas detection, and gas main failure prediction techniques sought to understand these processes. While helpful, the information did not lead to techniques that could accurately predict the future failure of specific gas mains in real time with the rigour necessary to prevent all gas explosions in customers' homes. It was also unclear if the assets would start to fail at an accelerated rate in the future, thereby creating an unmanageable risk to the public.

As a consequence, and in consultation with the Health and Safety Executive, a national long-term asset replacement programme was agreed with the economic regulator Ofgem. This programme aims to replace all of the most potentially dangerous assets by 2032. At present, the cost of this programme is several hundreds of millions of pounds per life saved but, in the absence of a rigorous understanding of precisely when and where each pipe will fail, the whole-sale replacement remains the only option. For someone who is certain they do not live near a gas supply pipe at risk or who is unaware of the issues this solution might appear expensive, and in that sense the service response is not efficient. However, the data and information for a more efficient approach that is as effective is not available. All stakeholders have agreed to this approach and that until other options become justifiable, it is necessary.

The extraordinarily high numbers of assets, their cumulative impact on service, the variety of intervention options that different teams can deliver and the strings of dependencies – all this makes data and information handling for utilities a key factor when considering organisational design.

The type of data needed depends on a complex mixture of corporate strategy, the economic and regulatory climate the utility operates in, the nature of the utility itself, its people, tools, systems and the degree of team working.

5.4 Conclusions

In this chapter we have examined the reasons why, in recent times, there has been a growing need for modern asset management systems. In order to help understand why companies in different sectors and geographies have responded to various pressures in such a variety of ways, we introduced the Asset Management Capability Model.

The Asset Management Capability Model defines the six factors of **climate, complexity, goals, tools, organisation** and **teams**. Together, these factors help define the type of asset management system an organisation needs and the capability and effectiveness of the system deployed. Each of these six factors and its role in defining the need for, and capability of, asset management systems are discussed in turn in the following chapters.

We also briefly explored the importance of information and data. With processes, the information and data in any business form the 'machine code' and help define how a business can operate, how it can be organised and the types of systems and tools it needs. For utilities – where the operation, repair and enhancement of enormous volumes of assets must be planned and delivered – the importance of information and data and the associated processes are paramount. This 'machine code' works behind and between the six factors in the asset management model and is the medium, or 'language', by which they communicate with each other.

The Business Climate in which Utilities Operate

6.0 Introduction

In previous chapters we explored the history of utilities, the different regulatory approaches and the nature of regulation in different countries. We then explored the scale of utilities, with a view to giving readers new to the subject an understanding of their nature. In chapter 5 we introduced the asset management capability model, which outlines the six factors that together define the type and nature of the asset management systems appropriate for a particular utility.

In this chapter, we look at the first of these six factors, namely **climate**. We will first define **climate** and then explore its impact on different utilities. In the following chapter we will move on to the second of the six factors, **complexity**. At that point we shall also explore the combined impact of external **climate** and internal utility **complexity**. Together these factors indicate the nature of the asset management systems that are appropriate and practical for a particular utility.

6.1 What do we mean by 'busines climate'?

An organisation's business climate is defined by the impact of those external factors that are difficult, if not impossible, for the business to change in the short term. For organisations making and selling products in a competitive market, their business climate will be defined by issues such as market growth, the state of the economy, the number of competitors, the basis of competition, the availability of skills and market share. It is important to undertake this analysis in each of the separate territories or markets in which the organisation trades.

For regulated utilities, the four most significant issues are economic regulation, quality regulation, the level of economic growth and reputation. The nature and significance of each of these four factors in defining the type and capability of a utility's asset management system is explored below:

1. **Economic regulation:** one purpose of economic regulation is to mimic competition and ensure customers who are supplied by a regulated monopoly get the right level of utility service at the right price. The economic regulators do this by defining the affordable level of performance customers require and creating incentives and penalties for the regulated utilities. In addition, the economic regulator limits funding and thus profitability while ensuring the utilities can secure funding for the often-large investment programmes they are required to deliver. As this book is about utility asset management and not corporate planning, issues such as the shortage of capital and negative inflation that reduces real utility funding are considered economic regulatory issues. This is because the economic regulator has a role to understand and respond (or decline to do so) to such issues at times of rate reviews or price reviews.

2. **Quality regulation** (environmental, health and safety, drinking water) defines the performance levels of utility networks and so drives the need for improvements or enhancements. For example the European Urban Waste Water Treatment Directive and the US Clean Water Act have resulted in the introduction of new consent standards at many waste water treatment works and, the need for large construction and enhancement programs. In the European

and North American gas industry, health and safety risk management has driven programs of work that require the replacement of iron gas mains to prevent and control explosion risk. In the water treatment sector, water treatment and distribution improvements are principally driven by potable water standards, leading to large programs of work to further reduce iron (cast iron mains replacement), arsenic (improved water treatment and new arsenic-free water sources and abandoning some older water sources) and Cryptosporidium and Giardia treatment and removal (improved filtering and disinfection). For rail, the nature, tone and challenge presented by customer service obligations – such as hourly passenger transit targets and track serviceability objectives – are important. Many of these factors can be very closely managed with the economic regulatory issues identified above.

3. **Economic growth:** Although the economic situation determines customers' willingness to pay for utility services, the balance of service and cost is a choice that must be determined by the economic regulator, albeit with much support from the utility companies themselves. Other critical impacts on utilities from economic growth are the levels of new connections and new utility services that need to be provided. In areas such as the Middle East, where provision of first-time utility services represents 50-90% of investment and activity, the most important challenge is to grow network capacity ahead of economic growth.

Case study 1: Allowing economic growth by modernising the waste water treatment network
A Middle Eastern waste water treatment company is building a large interceptor sewer and new waste water treatment plant in

the desert to transform a city's ability to connect many new developments to a municipal drainage system. The highly ambitious project will also allow a number of future developments currently under construction to proceed to completion and enable residents to move into their new homes. The interceptor will be used for storage at times of peak flow, has a diameter of over five metres at points and reaches depths of more than 70 metres below ground. The project represents enormous disturbance as its path is a block wide and passes through much of the city. Delivery of the project is a national priority and is complicated by undocumented drainage services and the need to provide effective drainage and treatment throughout the project.

The waste water treatment utility has many other general maintenance priorities. Although much of the sewage treatment network is relatively new, equipment that is adopted from property developers can sometimes prove substandard or ineffective and have hidden maintenance problems. However important those issues are, delivery of the new sewer interceptor and the new treatment works and pumping stations are critical to existing economic development projects being able to continue and city life to return to normal.

Even quite slow growth over a number of years can soak up spare network capacity and create hot spots that require expensive solutions. The great difficulty in securing land to site substations, overhead lines, sewage works, railways and highways means it takes longer to extend utility networks than it does for property developers to build and commission new buildings.

4. **Reputation:** The public reputation of a utility can affect transactions as varied as price review outcomes, industrial relations, and the ability of the organisation to secure

planning permissions and recruit talent. In Chapter 3 the change in the nature of a utility's relationship with the public when privatisation occurs was noted. However, a public reputation will be determined by the quality of customer service, something for which utilities, particularly larger ones, may have a poor delivery track record. Although certain organisational departments, such as billing and customer call centres, have a clear and direct impact on customer satisfaction, almost every member of staff working in a utility has the scope to enhance or degrade customer service. Quantifying customers' need for utility services and willingness to pay for the cost of these improvements is a critical process discussed in detail in Chapter 9. Organising the delivery of excellent customer service requires great attention to detail, leadership and careful process and tool design. Further discussion of this is outside the scope of this book and it is not considered further other than where companies' asset management systems must support such issues. It is worth noting that there is only a need for an asset management system and, for that matter, utility services of any type in order to serve their customers. A further cautionary observation is that utility staff can frequently forget that taking good care of their assets and taking good care of their customers is not always the same thing. The multi-disciplinary response and the leadership needed to address these issues means another book probably needs to be written on the subject by someone with insight into the issues.

The reputation of utilities can also be disproportionately shaped by the occurrence of several similar incidents in quick succession. This can lead to a 'special situation' in which the public or small groups of angry customers become sensitised to a particular issue. Clearly a train crash is always deeply regrettable, particularly when there are fatalities, and all steps should be taken to manage these risks. There is a low but real possibility two such incidents could occur in close proximity to each other. If such circumstances arise, the utility can find itself under immense pressure to make visible but sometimes unhelpful responses, even though rail transport remains one of the safest methods of travel.

Other examples of an aggravated climate for utilities include public anger to frequent odour problems emanating from a sewage works, hostility from small groups of customers repeatedly experiencing power interruptions, hosepipe bans in two consecutive years and consistent flooding of specific properties with sewage effluents. In all cases, there appears at first to be limited appetite from society to provide the enormous levels of funding needed to address these issues. But when a special situation occurs, exceptional levels of criticism arise and there is great pressure for a reactive solution. Utilities need to be exceptionally vigilant, thoughtful and responsive to the emergence of special situations while resisting the agendas of any groups that may be capitalising on the incident to achieve their local or narrow objectives.

Getting the balance right under such circumstances is a challenge that demands great skill, sensitivity and integrity. However, establishing asset management systems and tools that identify potential risks early is part of the solution and this is explored further in Chapter 9.

6.3 Why is business climate important?

The business climate defines the extent of the incentives and the penalties that encourage a particular utility to deliver the required cost and quality of services. The business climate creates a need to generate effective plans and, therefore, the need for appropriate asset management systems.

In the absence of any business complexity, the utility may respond to each element of business climate challenge with the required responses.

The more challenging a business climate, the more important it is for a business to undertake information processing. This may manifest itself in the increasing sizes of regulatory returns, as regulatory detail requires more information or larger numbers of project managers to work on an increasing number of projects. In the absence of complexity, which is discussed in the next chapter, the type of response called for by the business climate is clear even though delivery may be extremely difficult. Accordingly, the business climate can be addressed with more specialist functions and departments, which can focus on the challenges the organisation faces.

6.4 The impact of regulation on the business climate

The nature, methods, rigour and tone of regulation each play a key role in determining the business climate in which a utility operates.

Clearly, tone and nature of regulation can be significant, as the following case study illustrates.

Case study 2: Recollections of a waste water treatment manager
'Of course it used to be quite different [..] years ago. Before the [quality regulation organisation] was separated out from the [waste water treatment utility] there was a very different way of working. Minor plant failures really didn't help anyone. I always knew when the inspector was coming as he would call to ask me to put the kettle on. If I had a problem on the site I would take the sample myself, and, well, we didn't have a problem then. To be fair, if something went seriously wrong we all sorted it out and if it was serious we needed to get [sample] failures so we could build the business case for projects. We did have a time when inspectors had performance targets to get certain levels of failures. There was one inspector who was on a mission to get some type of

record by finding fault with everything, but that was all wrong too, and that was stopped after a while. People didn't really seem that bothered then, but it did mean you really didn't want to annoy an inspector.'

Industry structure and national policy determine the degree of challenge which economic and quality regulation exercise. An analysis of the effectiveness and rigour of economic regulation in different regions is both contentious and complex. Effective regulation can drive enhanced performance but excessive or inappropriate regulation can increase costs, have unintended consequences or create unmanageable risks which discourage investors. Such issues are better discussed by specialist regulatory studies. Figure 6.1 below highlights some of the factors that can signal and determine the nature of the regulatory climate in which a utility operates.

The regulatory business climate establishes fixed amounts of funding and specific outcomes that must be delivered during the regulatory period. This creates a need for managers to develop an asset management system that can plan and anticipate future costs, risks and outcomes with sufficient rigour and over the appropriate time period. The necessary capability of the asset management system is therefore strongly influenced by the length of the regulatory period and the consequences (rewards and penalties) for the utility if it cannot deliver agreed outcomes during that time. This is discussed further below.

A common fear of economic regulators is a situation of 'data asymmetry'. This can arise when regulators rely on the management of utilities to prepare all the information that informs a price review. Accordingly, there is the possibility that if the management looks hard enough, it can create a plausible, complex and comprehensive case for excessive funding allowances while the regulator will have little basis on which to challenge those proposals. As observed in Chapter 3, many regulators require price review plans and proposals

Enablers of enhanced regulatory rigour

Independence of a regulator: If an economic or quality regulator is independent of the utilities and of the state, more objective regulation can arise.

Price and service comparators: By comparing the service performance and efficiency of different utilities and punishing poor performers, a culture of improvement can be created.

Binding long term allowances: The use of binding five or more years service and funding plans and targets transfers the risk of unknown events to the utility.

Incentives: Allowing utilities to retain efficiencies and allowing incentives for good customer service encourages and rewards excellence.

Large organisational size: Large economic regulators or quality regulators regulating a single large national utility can make the culture of team working and mutual respect more difficult to establish and maintain.

Mechanisms and policy of fines and penalties: A track record of levying fines and penalties which are not recharged to customers indicates a signal failure to achieve the minimum standards is unacceptable.

Time: Over time, regulatory challenge and regulatory reporting become more complex as additional features are introduced.

Competition: Where customers must have choice or where concessions must be re-tendered, regulatory rigour can be enhanced. However, the real nature of the business climate can be measured by factors such as the number of times customers change supplier or contracts are tendered, the length of contract term, the number of bidders and the number of contracts re-let to the incumbent.

Ownership of utility assets: If the ownership of utility assets has become separated from the state, regulators will need to put in place regulatory mechanisms which ensure the serviceability of utility assets is maintained.

Privatisation of utilities: Where privatisation has occurred and utilities have the prospect of profiting from out-performance, regulators, policy makers and the public are less tolerant of service failures and this sets the tone of the regulatory climate.

Moderators of regulatory rigour

National champions: The existence of a policy to support and encourage national champions can make effective economic and quality regulation more difficult to establish.

Favorable long term regulatory contracts: If long term contracts are favorable to the utility the regulatory challenge process will not bite. This situation may prevail in a rate setting environment until either party triggers a rate review.

Small utilities: It is difficult to introduce rigorous evidence based regulation and asset management planning into a highly fragmented utility sector as the data and systems burden on the utility and the regulator would be unmanageable.

Customer and stakeholder support: Utilities which enjoy strong local stakeholder support are more likely to receive and deserve a more benign regulatory climate. This can be more difficult for larger utilities. Small utilities are more likely to have a strong local identity and customer-serving ethos which is helpful for preventing utility goals deviating far from those of the local community. Small utilities are more likely to be in regular contact with local stakeholders who may also wish to take an active role in approval of budgets and plans.

Local regulation: Rate setting or price review processes which involve frequent and close consultation with local political stakeholders can result in policy and funding decisions being made and re-made in local government organisations. Under such situations the utility becomes less accountable for service outcomes and the significance of the regulator/utility interface becomes less.

Figure 6.1 Enablers and moderators of regulatory rigour

to improve the use of forward-looking risk-based methodologies that are driven by auditable information and data, and so avoid the use of expert judgement.

As discussed earlier, a critical issue that determines the necessary capability of the asset management system is the time horizon of detailed and binding asset management plans. Clearly five to twenty five year strategic investment plans are essential for defining the scope and strategy for major investment plans. Where regulatory cycles require five-year plans with detailed and defined scope and fixed levels of funding, it sets exacting commercial demands on the capability and rigour of asset management systems. Where price review processes take two to three years, there is a requirement for utilities to produce detailed asset management investment plans for periods of up to six to eight years into the future. In practice, the preparation of plans can be made difficult by the late arrival in the process of regulatory investment targets, such as sewage works consents and river water quality objectives. As a consequence, asset management systems that are capable of flexible investment objectives and scenario analysis are helpful.

Case study 3: Impact of late changes to price review scope:
In the last few days of a price review and rate-setting process in the late 1990s, one waste water utility company was asked to include a programme of combined sewer/detention tank works that had been excluded previously. At the time, this was felt to be non-contentious since previous work of this type had progressed smoothly, so its inclusion at short notice was agreed.

In subsequent years, however, the ambitious sizes of some of these programmes radically changed the nature of the larger projects themselves. Previous experience of unit cost analysis indicated minor economies of scale were expected with size. But for large projects in some neighbourhoods, there came a point when the costs multiplied, such as when the size of assets started extending into bedrock, and enhanced screening and de-silting systems needed more complex power supplies and electricity connections. With hindsight, this late inclusion of scope was an error, not only for the utility but also for society and the environment. A number of the schemes became so expensive, their cost and carbon footprint far outweighed their environmental benefit.

In contrast, the rate setting regulatory processes, discussed in Chapter 3, invariably mean there is less need for a utility to prepare medium-term plans. This is particularly the case where utilities have the option of calling for a rate review if issues arise. It may be that the utility will seek to prepare medium-term asset management plans to aid delivery; however, these plans may have to be revised if future objectives, budgets and priorities are not anticipated.

Under such circumstances, it could be argued the asset management system has extended into areas outside the utility, including the organisations or the processes that undertake the rate review process. For example, even though the utility's plans and budgets are changed annually, there may be a need for a rigorous 'master plan' in the municipality which includes binding medium-term outcomes and budgets for all activities including the delivery of utility services. The reality, however, is such plans are of little commercial significance as there are no third parties, such as shareholders, who will fund deviations from the plan in the event of poor performance.

The consequences of these issues and the types of solutions to these pressures are discussed further in Chapters 9, 10 and 11.

A key commercial issue for utilities in mature economies that are also in a challenging business climate is to establish the right levels of asset replacement and capital maintenance budgets. As observed in Chapter 4, these activities are already costly and most commentators accept historical replacement investment must rise sharply at some point over the next twenty years. However with water, gas and electric utilities presenting calls for 40-100% increases in funding every five years, the challenge for utilities and the economic regulator is to prepare and scrutinise these forecasts and objectively establish how much more risk utilities should take in order to safely defer this investment into future regulatory periods. In order to do so, economic regulators and, indeed, the boards of utility companies have been using formal techniques to assess their view of the rigour and capability of utilities' asset management planning systems. In 2002, Ofgem's ARM (Asset Risk Management) survey assessed the electricity and gas distribution and transmission companies' asset management capability in the areas shown in Figure 6.2

The results of this comparative survey were published in December 2002 and although the report did not identify individual

---

Business strategy & direction

A1 Aims and objectives
A2 Identifying key issues for asset risk management
A3 Assigning accountabilities
A4 Structures and contracts
A5 Operating, integrating and interpreting
A6 Risk assessment and decision making
A7 Review process

Asset & network strategy

B1 From policy to procedure
B2 Defining asset life and serviceability
B3 Recording asset information
B4 Innovation and new technology
B5 Security of supply and asset utilisation
B6 Compliance with legislation

Asset life cycle management

C1 From procedure to delivery
C2 Asset register contents
C3 Utilisation
C4 Use of contractors/suppliers
C5 Inspection & maintenance regimes

Source: Ofgem 2002 Asset Risk Management Survey of British Electricity and Gas Distribution and Transmission Companies, Crown Copyright.

Figure 6.2 Asset Risk Management Capabilities explored in Ofgem's 2002 ARM survey

companies, the boards of those companies could establish their comparative capability in each of the study areas. The timing of the survey was also significant as it was undertaken shortly before the 2004 Price Review. As a consequence, a comparative below-average capability in one area could threaten to undermine the credibility of price review proposals which were due to be submitted in the following year. The significance of this was recognised by most utilities boards and there was a burst of activity ahead of the price review focused on improving data and system issues.

Case study 4: The impact of Ofgem's Asset Risk Management survey – one electricity industry executive recollection

'The ARM survey back in 2002 was actually quite helpful for us. Although several of the survey questions – such as those about double-checking of suppliers and contractors – seemed to encourage unnecessary bureaucracy, on the whole the survey was really helpful. We had asset data problems arising from the merger of our network with [..] and this was picked up. We had had many of these issues for some time and no one seemed to take them really seriously. With the ARM results, we found it much easier to get Board support for a range of actions which we pushed through that winter and that put us in much better position [for the Price Review].'

The growing number of asset management definitions and methodologies were becoming confusing for stakeholders and utility companies. In 2001, the Institute of Asset Management began its work to create an industry standard to define asset management capability. This culminated two years later in the publication of BSI PAS 55: 2004. This has become, along with its subsequent revision in 2008, an industry standard. In 2006, Ofgem launched an industry consultation process that led to the British gas and electricity industry agreeing to report progress in securing certification in accordance with the PAS 55 standard.

In the 2004 and 2009 English and Welsh water and waste water price reviews, Ofwat used a similar process to review the rigour used by utilities to compare their capital maintenance proposals.

Central to Ofwat's methodology was the assumption that low-scoring companies will tend to overestimate the level of capital maintenance. Accordingly, the score generated for each company's five-year capital maintenance plans for water distribution, waste water drainage, water treatment and waste water treatment were tracked.

At the 2004 price review, larger proportions of investment growth requested by high-scoring companies were allowed and less investment growth from low-scoring companies was approved. However, the importance of the capability scores water and sewage utilities received at the 2004 price review to fund the next five years went beyond the merely commercial. The companies were also categorised into one of five bands depending on their capability score. Only two companies managed to score in the highest banding – 'leading' – while the lowest two bands were described as 'below intermediate' and 'trailing'. These emotive descriptions gave the boards of water and waste water companies food for thought in the aftermath of the 2004 price review, with poorly performing companies seeking to improve systems and reorganise and recruit to address those shortcomings.

At the 2009 price review, the 28 criteria detailed in Figure 6.3 were given a variety of weightings and used to assess and score the rigour of companies' five-year capital maintenance investment plans.

By the 2009 price review the capabilities of the water, waste water and electricity distribution companies' asset management systems had substantially improved. However, a large gap remains between the levels of funding the economic regulators sanction and the levels of investment requested by the utilities. This gap is worrying and all parties need a deeper, shared understanding of the facts and consequences. The pragmatic application of asset management planning systems will help us move towards that goal.

Factor

Company engagement with customers and other stakeholders

Choice of planning objectives

Valuation of service benefits

Governance

Policy

Strategy

People management

Integration (of price review processes) into routine business processes

Planning processes

Information management processes

Quality assurance

Systems for capturing and storing asset performance and condition data

Systems to support risk management processes & reporting

Asset observations

Serviceability data and associated costs

Interventions and impact data and associated costs

Historical analysis

Performance modelling

Service consequence modelling

Cost consequence modelling

Forecast service

System analysis

Intervention identification

Intervention impacts

External reporting

Overall balance and phasing of plan

Overall approach to risk

Overall quality of the business case

Figure 6.3 Criteria used by Ofwat to assess the rigour of English and Welsh water and waste water companies' capital maintenance investment plans at the 2009 price review

6.5 Characterisation of the business climate experienced by different utility sectors and the significance of climate

A characterisation of the degree of challenge arising from the nature of the business climate which different utility industries experience is included in figure 6.4.

In addition to the factors identified above, the additional regulatory issues listed in Figure 6.1 may be expected to enhance or moderate the demands of the business climate on the utility.

For utilities in challenging business climates, there is a greater need for them to have more control over their business or, as case study 3 illustrated, be able to respond more quickly to events. For industries such as power generation and gas distribution and transmission, this reflects a need for firm control over asset and process risk. For utilities experiencing binding long-term regulatory contacts or high levels of new asset build, such as electricity transmission or water or waste water utilities, medium- and long-term asset plans are needed.

6.6 Conclusions

In this chapter we explored the nature and significance of the first of the six factors included in the Asset Management capability model: **climate**.

For utilities, the **climate** is the business environment in which the utility operates and is the equivalent of the market and economic environment within which a traditional trading business operates. For utilities, the key drivers of **climate** are economic and quality regulation. In some regions, such as the Middle East, the need to establish large numbers of new connections can be the single most important priority. The reputation of the company and its track record in delivering good customer service also colour the public's response to events.

Key	Criteria	Explanation
1. European & North American gas distribution	Very High	Gravity of the Health & Safety (Explosion) risk to customers imposes a requirement for very high levels of auditable operational control. In the event of an incident all asset management and operational decisions may be critically examined with a view to establishing asset data or management errors.
		Extensive cast iron replacement programme underway and delivery is a priority. The rules are prescriptive and provided the rules of this regime are followed the asset management challenge is very simple.
		Low reinforcement needs but spare network capacity becoming used up.
2. European & North American gas transmission	Very High	Gravity of the health & safety (Explosion) risk to customers and the criticality of the equipment imposes a requirement for very high levels of auditable operational control and equipment design and maintenance.
3a and 3b. European & North American electricity distribution	Medium-High	Growing threat of external factors such as distributed generation.
		Cumulative effect of CML (Customer Minutes of Lost supply) and CI (Customer Interruptions) closely regulated.
		Companies at the low end of this range (3b) are those where rate setting/funding is done regularly, sometimes annually, by regulators or political leaders who share accountability with the company for operational outcomes.
4. Middle Eastern electricity distribution	Very High	High economic growth & large number of new connections urgently calling for first-time services.
		Cumulative effect of CML (Customer Minutes of Lost supply) and CI (Customer Interruptions) closely regulated.
5 European & North American electricity transmission	High	Connection of wind & other new generation sources creating substantial network issues.
		Supply chain issues.
6. Middle Eastern electricity transmission	High	High economic growth & large number of new connections.
		Supply chain issues.
7. Canals and waterways	Low	The largely static nature of these assets, very low growth and choice many users have to use these facilities gives this industry a stable and subdued business climate. Some inhabitants and long-time residents can be highly aggressive to canal owners and operators and levels of charges but such stakeholders are a small minority.
8a and 8b. European & North American water distribution & treatment	Medium-High	High operational standards to ensure and demonstrate biological and chemical quality of potable water in treatment and distribution.
		Companies at the higher end of this range (8a) would include companies where there are large numbers of new treatment standards which require considerable numbers of treatment plant and distribution equipment rebuilding.
		Companies at the low end of this range (8b) are those where rate setting/funding is done regularly, sometimes annually, by regulators or political leaders who share some accountability with the company for operational outcomes.
9. Middle Eastern water distribution	High	High economic growth & connections.
10. European & North American sewage drainage and treatment	High	Weather events and large number of new environmental standards.
11. Middle Eastern sewage drainage & treatment	Very High	High economic growth & connections.
12. Power generation	Very High	Extremely high cost of equipment down time and high fixed costs.
13. Rail	Very High - Medium	The public visibility of performance and the need to manage severe health and safety issues introduces considerable tension. The high cost of downtime (network failure for two hours at peak loading can cost £'m) which can be easily quantified and managed imposes demanding regime on network operators.
		In this traditional industry the political and regulatory business climate may be particularly moderated or aggravated by industrial relations and labour issues. This can result in a wide range of business climates in which the industry must operate.

Figure 6.4 The relative severity of the business climate in which different utility industries operate

In Figure 6.1, we looked at the features of regional and national regulation that can enhance or relax the **climate** in which a utility operates. We then explored the actual mechanisms economic regulators in the UK have used to ensure investment proposals are of sufficient quality and rigour. The net result of this has been two-fold. In the first instance, stretching performance targets and funding allowances were agreed between regulators and utility companies in extremely complex circumstances. In the second instance, the boards of utility companies were keen to implement asset management systems that give them visibility of risk and cost, enabling them to control and manage those risks proactively.

Finally, we characterised the varying challenges business **climate** can present to utilities. In the next chapter we shall explore the second of the six factors within the asset management capability model, utility **complexity**. Together, **climate** and **complexity** are key factors in determining which asset management system is right for a particular utility.

7 Utility Complexity

7.0 Introduction

In Chapter 5 we introduced the asset management capability model, which holds the six factors that together define the type and nature of the asset management systems appropriate for a particular utility.

In the previous chapter we looked at the first of these six factors, **climate**, and its role in defining the need for good control over utility process risk and plans. In this section we look at the role the second of the six factors, **complexity**, plays in constructing a suitable and effective asset management system.

We do so by first exploring the relative **complexity** of a range of utility sectors and finally the impact of **complexity** and **climate** in determining the types of asset management systems appropriate for different utilities.

7.1 Size and scale

An extremely simple indicator of the complexity of a utility asset base is its size, which reflects the numbers of transactions and activities that are necessary to maintain and operate a utility network. For the smallest utilities, typically those serving 30,000 households or less, it is possible for a small, highly experienced operational team that has a great deal of local knowledge and works well together to have a subjective view of where risk lies and what needs to be done next. Above that size, however, the complexity and scale of even the simplest utility systems make proactive utility management and medium-term planning impossible without some elements of a formal asset management system.

Utility networks also vary in density and complexity within a particular region. Accordingly, the estimated replacement values for key utility sectors included in Chapter 3 Figure 3.1 give an indication of the relative scale and complexity of utility sectors. This comparison highlights the significance of waste water, and to a lesser extent water, which together account for two-thirds of the utility assets in a region and, therefore, a high concentration of complexity.

Although the replacement value of utility assets is a helpful measure, it is only a part of the story as assets and utility networks have different levels of criticality and varying lives. For example, sewers and drains, which by value typically account for a third of the utility infrastructure in a region, are fairly static assets with long lives. However, as seen in Chapter 4, a blockage or collapse at any point on a sewer network can lead to storm waters accumulating, bursting out of any of hundreds of thousands of manhole covers and flooding customers' homes.

In contrast, the mechanical and electrical element of pumping stations on a sewer network may only represent a tiny fraction of the network's replacement value and yet these are much shorter-life assets, operating in a tough environment and requiring much attention to ensure performance. The following section explores the internal complexity of key utility sectors in different geographies and details a comparative benchmarking of utility complexity.

7.2 Characterisation of utility complexity

Figure 7.1 characterises the internal complexity of the key utility sectors serving the inhabitants of a region or city.

Key	Criteria	Explanation
1. European & North American gas distribution	Medium	Relatively simple asset base with low pressures but fragile assets. The methodologies for assessing criticality of gas mains are well understood and so the gas mains replacement planning process (which accounts for 90% of investment) is critical but not complex. Need to efficiently manage large numbers of critical assets and less critical assets introduce some difficult policy options. Severe customer gas safety issues impose operational complexity not asset planning issues.
2. European & North American gas transmission	Low-Medium	High pressures, Critical assets. However, imperative to treat all assets as critical makes decision making easier. Relatively modest numbers of assets. Relatively young and standardised asset base.
3a & 3b. European & North American electricity distribution	High-Medium	Standardised assets, generally good data, predictable behaviours of assets but ageing asset base. Large numbers of assets. Customers may notice even very momentary interruptions to supply, thereby making system operation and flexibility key issues. The interactions between different voltages make reinforcement more complex and contentious. Networks serve rural and urban areas and high connection rates are typical. Companies at the top end of this range (3a) are larger electricity companies who may be dealing with over 100,000 households. The larger size leads to increased levels of interconnection and more complexity and numbers of options for load planning.
4. Middle Eastern Electricity Distribution	Medium	Standardised assets, generally good data, and predictable behaviours of assets. Some assets becoming aged. Quality of assets adopted from developers variable. Large numbers of assets. Networks serve rural and urban areas and high connection rates are typical. Customers may notice even very momentary interruptions to supply, thereby making system operation and flexibility key issues. High consumption for air conditioning can make loads variable.
5 European & North American electricity transmission	Medium-High	Many Transmission Assets are critical assets. However, imperative to treat all assets as critical makes decision making easier. Ageing asset base. Relatively modest numbers of assets. High complexity of undertaking reinforcement.
6. Middle Eastern Electricity Transmission	Medium	Many Transmission Assets are critical assets. Critical assets. However imperative to treat all assets as critical makes decision making easier. Relatively modest numbers of assets. Very High complexity of undertaking reinforcement
7. Canals and waterways	Low	Old static civil assets.

Figure 7.1 Characterisation of utility complexity

Key	Criteria	Explanation
8. European & North American water distribution & treatment	High	Complexity of controlling numerous treatment processes and network issues.
		Very large numbers of assets.
		Companies at the top end of this range are larger water companies who may be dealing with over 500,000 households.
9. Middle Eastern Water Distribution	Low	Requirement for local domestic storage removes criticality of temporary outages. Also lack of water treatment in this utility type.
		The political and environmental issues arising from national competition for water resources are political issues and are disregarded in this context.
10. European & North American sewage drainage and treatment	Very High	Exceptionally large numbers of assets & large number of old non-standardised treatment assets and old networks make capital maintenance planning difficult.
		Growing complexity of new biological and chemical treatment processes makes process control more sensitive. Also addition of new processes to old plant imposes asset management, construction and subsequent operating challenges.
		Fixed nature of the sewer networks and need to maximise use of land gradients impose practical constraints.
		Semi-chaotic biological processes impacted by temperature and toxicity of discharges to sewers by Industry and by the sewer network and treatment capacity.
		Sewage Sludge Treatment and recycling/disposal impose complexity and dependences.
11. Middle Eastern sewage drainage & treatment	High	Semi-chaotic biological processes impacted by temperature and toxicity and septicity of discharges to sewers by customers and by the sewer network to treatment capacity.
		Exceptionally large numbers of assets.
		Complex interaction between treatment and drainage and impact of high temperatures on biological treatment.
		Combination of relatively new assets but mixture of build quality of treatment and pumping assets adopted from property developers introduces complexity.
		Sewage Sludge Treatment and recycling/disposal impose complexity and dependencies.
		Additional complexity of waste water recycling and reuse for irrigation and cooling water.
12. Power generation	Low	Although power plant is complex and of high value plant is well supervised, standardised, and located at a small number of sites and highly automated with extensive use of automated process control systems.
13. Rail	Low-Medium	The visible and linear nature of many assets, their high value and close supervision makes their inspection and management less challenging.
		Complexity introduced by some asset classes such as Stations and Signalling and opex and capex options.

Figure 7.1 (continued)

7.3 The significance of utility complexity

Utility complexity is important as it creates interdependencies between different issues and decision-making becomes harder. 'Complexity' also does this quite aggressively, with a doubling of complexity making it four times harder to establish the best outcome.

Information may need to be collected from a number of different work groups to enable effective decisions. In deciding how the performance of a particular asset may be enhanced, for example, a view needs to be taken on the current performance risk of the asset, the cost and benefit of all replacement, refurbishment and replacement options, and the merits of all competing projects. For a complex system, this can be a challenge.

> *Case study 1: Understanding the full complexity of asset decisions*
>
> *The contracts established by an electricity utility for wood pole[1] replacement costs provided for more than what was needed for this particular type of work. In itself this is not unusual – in any basket of operational targets and contractor rates, individual items may cost more or less than allowances, although the package as a whole will have been tendered and won by the lowest cost bid. However, a combination of poor wood pole condition data, a culture of very high workmanship and poor contractor control meant little control over local decision making.*
>
> *As the months went by, large numbers of wood poles began to be replaced. The long life and complexity of such refurbishment projects and the practice of giving old poles to farmers in return for prompt land access meant it was hard to check if the poles actually needed replacing. As a consequence, it took two years to recognise the issue, during which time average refurbishment costs for overhead lines doubled to £3,800 per 100 meters. Staff felt it was cheaper to replace assets while they were*

on site and they felt the network would operate better and more cheaply in storm conditions. However, they did not see the lost value of replacing an asset that, in all probability, had many years of service life remaining. They were also unaware of the projects in other parts of the corporation that could not be funded that year.

[1] Wood poles are the wooden posts that support high and low voltage overhead power lines in rural areas. They are particularly sensitive assets as a poorly maintained wood pole network can suffer wide scale storm or ice damage.

Getting visibility of all the important factors is often difficult but increased utility complexity makes it much more so. The following section looks at the cumulative impact of two of the factors in the asset management capability model, namely climate and complexity. We look at how these factors combine to define the type of asset management system needed by a utility.

7.4 The cumulative impact of climate and complexity

A relaxed business climate means there is less need to plan, either because the environment is calm (and budgets need only be adjusted by inflation) or because stakeholders are comfortable setting budgets and performance levels year by year in the light of events. High complexity means the future may be different to the past. Figure 7.2 characterises the cumulative impact of climate and complexity on utilities into one of four types, referred to as 'calm', 'tourist', 'stressed' or 'campaign'.

Figure 7.3 characterises the impacts of climate and complexity on different utilities industries. In this figure we have combined the characterisation of utility sector climate undertaken in Figure 6.4 from chapter 6 and the analysis of internal complexity detailed in Figure 7.1 of this chapter into one diagram.

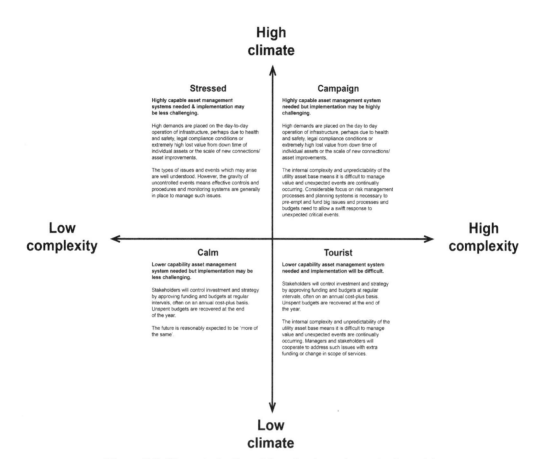

Figure 7.2 Characterisation of the climate and complexity matrix

Utility companies towards the top of the diagram are in a challenging climate and they are located in the 'stressed' or 'campaign' zones detailed in Figure 7.2. They are exposed to factors such as a challenging regulatory environment, where failure to deliver specific levels of performance or safety over long-term fixed price regimes is punished and/or there is a need to extend or enhance the performance of the network. As a consequence, these companies need asset risks to be tightly understood and controlled and robust long-term plans to be available.

Utilities to the right of the diagram operate and own volatile and unpredictable networks. Problems and issues are often 'knotty',

Climate \ Complexity	Low	Low/Medium	Medium	Medium/High	High	Very High
Very High	12 Power generation	2 European & North American gas transmission 13a Rail	1 European & North American gas distribution 4 Middle Eastern electricty distribution		11 Middle Eastern sewage treatment	
High	9 Middle Eastern water	13b Rail	6 Middle Eastern electricity transmission	5 European & North American electricity transmission 3a European & North American electricity distribution	8a European & North American water treatment & distribution	10 European & North American sewage treatment
Medium		13c Rail	3b European & North American electricity distribution		8b European & North American water treatment & distribution	
Low	7 Canals & Waterways					

Figure 7.3 Relative complexity of different utility sectors

systems need to be complex, and team working is needed to ensure plans accommodate all the needs of the business. For example, growth in load from increasing use of air conditioning equipment in cities may be accommodated by the spare substation capacity that exists in summer months. However, a combination of higher summer temperatures and high loads can result in equipment cooling problems, which lead to shorter asset lives. In addition, the lack of a low load summer season on the network means certain complex maintenance tasks, which require key assets to be taken off line, cannot be scheduled and all equipment becomes marginally more critical.

7.5 Asset management system design

For utilities that are located towards the 'stressed' or 'campaign' areas detailed in Figure 7.2, regulatory and market forces mean there is a need for more capable asset management systems. For those companies in the 'campaign' or 'tourist' zones, the complexity of the utilities means there are greater difficulties in establishing these asset management systems.

Lastly, although companies in the 'tourist' and 'calm' zones do not face external regulatory pressures to prepare binding long-term asset management plans and budgets, the leadership of these utilities may choose to do so. This will be discussed further in the next chapter on organisational goals.

The tools used by utilities to prepare asset plans, control work and manage asset construction work are discussed in Chapter 9. However, Figure 7.4 details the most important types of asset

Figure 7.4 Illustrating the impact of climate and complexity on the need for different elements of the asset management system

management planning activities in each of the four asset management zones that a utility may have to undertake.

7.6 Conclusions

Recognising that the introduction of robust asset management systems is more difficult to achieve in a more complex utility, we explored the **complexity** of different utility industries. We also combined this analysis with the results from Chapter 6 to illustrate the cumulative impact of **climate** and **complexity** on the types of asset management systems that are needed. Figure 7.5 summarises the characteristics of key utility sectors on a business **climate** and business **complexity** map.

Individual utility companies may be expected to fall towards the top or right of their industry grouping when regulation is robust and challenging, utilities are larger or high levels of new growth and improved quality of services are required.

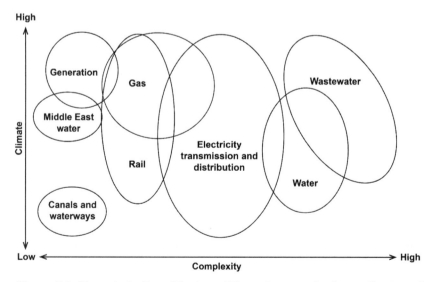

Figure 7.5 Characterisation of the key utility sectors on a business climate and complexity map

Figure 7.2 identifies the four asset management zones that characterise the types of response a utility exhibits if it is reactive or defensive by nature. Clearly, management may choose to be more proactive or assertive if it considers there are benefits in doing so.

In the following four chapters the roles of the remaining four factors – **goals, tools, organisation** and **teams** – in the asset management capability model are explored.

8 Corporate Goals

8.1 Introduction

Corporate **goals** are the third of the six factors included in the asset management capability model. In this chapter we explore how a utility's approach to defining its **goals** influences the types of asset management systems appropriate to it.

There is a degree of subjectivity in deciding what types of objectives and targets can be called **goals**. For the purpose of this book the implications of delivering the **goals** of efficiency and effectiveness, while protecting moral objectives such as health and safety, are explored.

Many organisations have a joint **goal** to achieve high efficiency and high effectiveness. However, efficiency and effectiveness are different things and are achieved in different ways. Furthermore, they can create conflicts that require imagination and insight to reconcile. The key purpose of the asset management system is to allow managers, directors and other stakeholders to understand where cost, risk and value lie in a utility – and so manage any conflicts between efficiency and effectiveness – while ensuring compliance with health and safety and other moral objectives.

8.2 Definitions of efficiency and effectiveness

High efficiency requires the careful use of resources to optimise delivery of the required outcomes. Accordingly, rationing and budgeting the provision of resources and inputs to a utility's processes are helpful in achieving efficiency. It can often be achieved by concluding a series of fine adjustments and optimisations. Examples of strategic methods used to improve efficiency include the regulatory mechanisms such as the RPI-x or certain rate review processes which were explored in chapter 3. On a more tactical level, the use of overtime restrictions, head count limits, financial budgets and 'stretch' budgets are all highly effective tools in helping business leaders control and ration resources.

In contrast, high effectiveness requires a focus on producing the right 'effects', or outcomes, products or services. In traditional service or manufacturing businesses, providing new services or innovative new features are strategies that companies may adopt to enhance the effectiveness of their product offering. In the utility sector, the creation of regulatory incentives linked to customer service outcomes, such as numbers of sewer flooding events or power outages, can enhance utility effectiveness. In addition, rate review processes in which great focus is placed on customer rates and tariffs can be very helpful at ensuring utilities make the delivery of effectiveness a principal goal of the business.

8.3 Achieving efficiency in utilities

High levels of efficiency are more easily attainable by the larger utilities, which benefit from economies of scale and substantial supply chain advantages. For the purpose of this book, larger utilities are considered to be utilities supplying more than 100,000 customers, and smaller utilities may be those utilities supplying populations of 30,000 or less.

Following privatisation and the regulation of many utilities across the world in the 1990's, the business climate in which utilities operated changed, as seen in Chapter 6. It became much more challenging, while these same companies realised substantial efficiency improvements. As was noted in Chapter 3, when efficient regulation exists, it results in enormous benefits for customers. In

1989/90 in England and Wales, for example, the new economic regulatory regime introduced a range of efficiency penalties for overspending allowances and incentives for delivering projects while under-spending regulatory targets. Relatively low priority was given in early regulation to guaranteed standards in electricity distribution and quality and service outcomes in water and sewerage.

As a consequence, a prime goal for many English and Welsh utilities at that time was an improvement in efficiency. These efficiencies were achieved by changing work practices, standardising equipment, applying lean techniques to improve processes, and introducing work management and scheduling techniques that improved performance management. Figure 8.1 below illustrates the journey many UK utilities took in the years following privatisation on an efficiency and effectiveness map.

The application of regulatory efficiency drivers also has resulted,

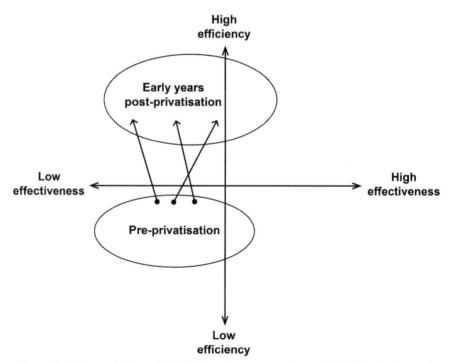

Figure 8.1 The early impact of efficiency improvements on UK utilities in the early years following privatisation

on occasion, in unfortunate outcomes. In the UK electricity and gas industries, regulatory pressures and market fragmentation led to the almost complete halt of research, which was only arrested by the introduction of a special regulatory measure to support innovation. Meanwhile, Professor Martin Cave observes in his Independent Review of Competition and Innovation in Water Markets[1] that the regulatory instruments that had driven water companies' focus on efficiency had similarly unforeseen outcomes in the UK water and waste water industry. Figure 8.2, reproduced from this report, illustrates the initial rise in research investment following privatisation and also a subsequent decline.

It is notable that a significant reduction in research and development occurred in 2000 following the 1999 price review, generally recognised as being harsh and which resulted in particular[2]

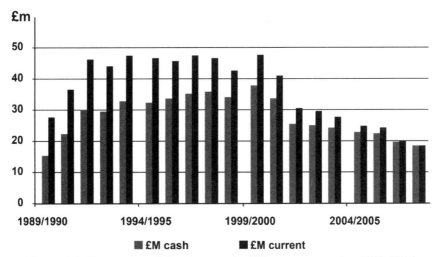

Figure 8.2 Research and development by UK water companies 1989-2007

[1] Independent Review of Competition and Innovation in the water markets: Crown Copyright, http://www.defra.gov.uk/environment/water/ industry/cavereview/pdf/cavereview-finalreport.pdf

[2] F Erbetta, M Cave, "Regulation and Efficiency Incentives: Evidence from the England and Wales Water and Sewerage Industry", Review of Network Economics. Vol.6 (4), 2007 pp 425-452, <http://www.rnejournal.com/artman2/ uploads/1/erbetta_et_al_RNE_dec07.pdf>

efficiency gains. This reduction in research and development investment undermined the industry's long-term efficiency and effectiveness.

Within utility organisations, efficiency can also be ineffectively delivered. Measures intended to introduce efficiencies for more complex utilities, many believe, actually produce unwelcome side effects that undermine performance. Most utility staff can identify examples of such events and while they are relatively infrequent, they do define the limits of best practice and result in considerable additional cost and reworking. Included below are three examples taken from different utilities, which illustrate the practical challenges of introducing asset management and performance measures that consistently deliver real efficiency.

Case study 1: Waste water utility seeking to contract out routine maintenance

A newly appointed director for a waste water utility sought greater efficiency by subcontracting routine work. Several contracts had already been very successfully let with substantial efficiency gains, often following resistance from managers. The next proposal was to sublet a contract for inspections and basic repairs to waste water pumping stations. Following the procurement process, a contract was let and work commenced. The contractor had an incoming inventory, decision trees, agreed schedules of work and capex and opex budgets. Initially all seemed well, with large numbers of inoperable standby pumps identified and promptly fixed by the contractor. However, as time passed, it became apparent there were significant errors on the asset register and the work mix wasn't as anticipated. Matters seemed to settle down after the first winter and underlying performance seemed to be acceptable, if exceptional events were ignored.

However, two years later and after several staff changes, a number of problems arose. Initially, there were complaints that screenings and silt from pumping stations were being flushed into the network during cleaning, leading to blinding of inlet screens at the treatment works. In addition, several serious waste water pumping station flooding incidents led to an internal investigation. The initial problems with the pumping station asset records were more serious than previously thought and, accordingly, the starting inventory was not meaningful. In addition, a continuing culture of hostility towards the contractor from some utility staff made it impossible to establish the facts of the issue. The contractor considered the initial asset inventory and condition assessments to be wrong, and the indicative framework budgets in the contract insufficient. The utility's maintenance manager also felt certain serious dereliction now existed and that over-maintenance had occurred at a smaller number of easy access pumping stations. The matter came to a head when disputed asset information meant the utility found it difficult to defend itself in a pumping station flooding prosecution.

In any event, notice was served on the contractor, who bitterly withdrew from the contract. Two years of maintenance records were lost and an expensive survey of the entire stock of pumping stations was necessary. This new survey identified a further 22 pumping stations that had not been on the records. Several utility supervisors and union leaders were to use this unhappy experience for some time to caution against any form of utility subcontracting work.

Case study 2: electricity distribution utility preparing for a price review

An electricity distribution utility was keen to enhance efficiency. Fourteen months earlier, the board had approved headcount restrictions and now the company was focused on ensuring the work bank of schemes being fed into construction delivery was quickly built up. Clearly, these measures were essential but the head of the asset management department was deeply worried. His network reinforcement plans for the next price review were nine months behind schedule and the most recent unit cost benchmarks were not available.

Over the last 12 months he had lost 14 people, which represented nearly 20% of his total head count. He replaced people as best as he could but he still had three vacancies in his network strategy department alone. Although his boss recognised the growing gravity of the situation and was supportive, it generally took 10 weeks to get permission to reappoint and finally get someone (anyone!) in, and a further four months for the new person to settle in. The head of asset management felt there were three root causes to his problems:

1. *The engineers making the really strategic decisions often have 30 years' service and keep retiring!*
2. *How can I get permission to raise pay to keep my most experienced people? Human Resources is concerned special pay rates will set a precedent. They may be right but…!*
3. *Designers keep leaving us for the construction department. This might be a promotion for them but I keep losing my most experienced people.*

The issue was resolved just in time for the price review by the recruitment of a number of specialist agency staff, one of whom had retired some time ago from the company. It was an expensive solution. The charge-out rates were high and essential knowledge of the programme build for the next price review was lost from the company. For this critical team, being effective was of prime importance as the team's annual cost was insignificant in comparison with the added value it had to deliver. Its search for efficiency had not delivered any efficiency benefits and the effectiveness of the entire utility had been threatened.

Case study 3: Maintenance of the site road at a water treatment works

The budget for routine maintenance was cut as part of a programme of efficiency measures for the last two years of a price review period at this water treatment works. The site manager intended to patch up the lengthy access road that had been deteriorating over the last few years but, in the face of the deep funding cuts, he agreed to delay the repairs for another 24 months. The site staff were not impressed. The expected repairs had been delayed twice already and several times they had taken it upon themselves to fill in the expanding potholes with road stone supplied by contractors visiting the site. If the manager felt the road could last another two years they felt it was best to see if he was right. Besides, the overtime ban made it that much harder to find time for additional tasks such as this.

That winter, operating issues resulted in a doubling of tanker movements on the site road. A combination of the extra traffic loading from the vacuum tankers and heavy snow and ice opened up three of the potholes and the vacuum tanker drivers, who owned their own vehicles, started complaining again. At the next inspection by the waste regulation agency, the inspector's attention was drawn to the potholes on the site road. As the vacuum tankers were carrying waste liquids, she instructed urgent road repair measures in accordance with the site's waste management plan for repair and resurfacing of the listed defects on the entire road.

The work had to be completed within 12 weeks and ended up costing $163,000, which was many times the cost of the original planned pothole repairs. Fortunately for the site manager, the road works were of such a scale they were funded by someone else's budget. Accordingly, he managed to get his road repaired and achieved his budget for operating costs that year. But it was not an efficient use of scarce investment funding.

These are examples where the narrow pursuit of efficiency proved a false economy. Such examples are greatly outnumbered by hard-won efficiency measures that improve the cost effectiveness of services for the benefit of customers. The ambition of properly functioning utilities is to have tools, performance systems, lean processes and organisational structures and cultures that allow them to achieve true efficiency. These issues are discussed in the following three chapters.

The economies of scale, supply chain benefits and specialisation have all allowed larger utilities to realise significant efficiency gains. Different strategies can be taken by smaller utilities to achieve efficiency. The sharing of central services – such as billing, control rooms or central purchasing agreements – can all be used to realise efficiency. Such measures, however, invariably lead to a complete merging of operations in the course of time.

8.4 Achieving effectiveness in utilities

It can be argued that effectiveness is the most important goal for a utility, as 'outcomes' are for customers. Yet this is an oversimplification. A focus on efficiency is also necessary to deliver aspects of effectiveness, such as affordability. In addition, there are different types of effectiveness and not all of them are in the true interests of customers. For example, short-term effectiveness, such as the targeting of low charges and high quality of services, may be unsustainable. Such a situation occurred in the Californian energy crisis in 2000/01. In theory, short-term effectiveness may also be appropriate for those customers who have no interest in the continuing health of the supplier. But such 'bargain hunting' is not practical with regulated utility businesses – long-term effectiveness is generally in the real interest of all customers.

Small utilities are more likely to invoke a strong association with customers and have a greater focus on effectiveness, often because they are local. They may also have less specialisation and operate flat management structures, in which case more employees will have daily contact with customers. Examples of such utilities may be the smaller of the 30,000 French water and waste water companies, smaller North American electricity distribution networks and many of the 700 multi-utilities that provide services to many German cities. The single employee of one Canadian utility, with just 680 customers, claimed to know most of his customers personally.

Another example of effective working was recently demonstrated by a small German multi-utility that was exploring smart metering technology. Smart metering is a new and complex subject. Throughout Europe and North America, large numbers of smart metering trials and deployments have been undertaken with, as yet, unclear outcomes. Although there are clear national energy efficiency policy benefits for smart metering, and power suppliers see major marketing opportunities from the technology, the benefits for customers remain unclear. A small German utility undertook a modest trial of several hundred units and then explored the benefits to its customers. This revealed a number of principles that have helped define smart metering effectiveness. Early on in the trial, for example, the trial manager noticed high, sustained levels of energy usage from an elderly lady's flat so he alerted her son that something did not seem right. The son visited his mother to discover that, some weeks before, she had placed a number of electric heaters in an upstairs toilet to protect against frost in a cold spell. Alarmed at the discovery of this and relieve the potential of fire have been avoided meant the son became a great champion of the new system in the local community.

In another situation, a customer with a reputation for being difficult refused to pay his bill. The utility manager warned the customer over the phone that his power would automatically be disconnected through the smart meter technology 'in five minutes' if he did not pay. While the customer continued to argue, his power was, as promised, disconnected. Later that morning, he settled his bill. This approach to customer service is extremely dangerous unless a great deal is known about the customer's circumstances and history and it is unlikely a larger company will find such approaches easy or safe to manage. In contrast small utilities may find a lack of economies of scale means unit costs for equipment and services may be double that of larger utilities and, accordingly, effectiveness may be achieved at the expense of efficiency.

But with good leadership and excellent process design and systems, large utilities can also achieve effectiveness if it is a priority, as the following case study illustrates.

Case study 4: The water utility that nearly ran out of water
After a drought that had lasted for 30 months, critical reservoirs operated by a water utility were becoming dangerously low. In response, the utility commenced importing water by road tankers and there was a media campaign to urge customers to save water and preparations were made to allow the introduction of 'standpipes'. A public outcry ensued, which was inflamed by a senior director of the utility commenting to the media that he left the region in order to take a bath. In making this statement, he had tried to emphasise his deep regret at the situation and his own readiness to take action to conserve scarce water stocks. Understandably, but unfairly, the public reacted angrily to these comments and took the view that while he may be prepared to drive 80 miles for a bath, all other customers felt this was completely unacceptable.

By the time the drought was over, tankering costs had risen to more than £40m, the company's reputation was in tatters, the share price collapsed and a shareholder revolt saw much of the senior leadership team replaced. At that time, the company could be considered as existing in a very highly challenging business climate of the nature discussed in Figure 6.4 in Chapter 6. In the following years, as the company rebuilt its reputation in the face of considerable public hostility, it adopted a commitment to customer focused effectiveness. Within a few years, the company scored top for customer service and upper quartile for regulatory efficiency and it has since continued to do so.

8.5 The efficiency and effectiveness mix

If a utility is not continually challenged by its management to deliver improved efficiency and effectiveness, its comparative performance will decline. This may occur because the climate in which a particular utility operates is benign, so management is not called upon to improve performance. Alternatively, it may be that the business management team is unable to deliver the performance required and, compared to other utilities, the organisation is considered to be failing. Or it may be that performance and effectiveness have improved, giving managers a false sense of comfort. However, these measures are comparative with higher levels of performance achieved by leading organisations. Similarly, all other things being equal, a smaller, well-run utility is more likely to be highly effective while a larger, well-managed utility has more opportunity to be highly efficient. These options are illustrated in Figure 8.3.

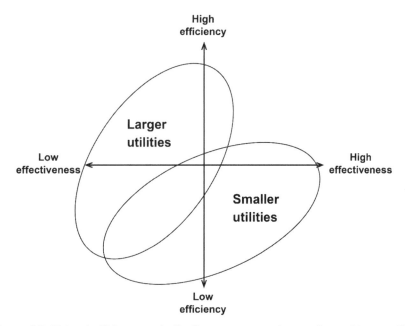

Figure 8.3 Natural efficiency and effectiveness spaces for smaller and larger utility organisations

Although it is the utility's choice to establish goals which target the appropriate levels of efficiency and effectiveness, a particular utility with a certain calibre of management team, a certain degree of complexity and level of capability in its asset management systems may adopt over time any one point on one of the lines shown in Figure 8.4.

In that diagram, the line labelled Utility A seeks to define the options a utility with low capability may, over time, adopt. For such a business, the two extremes of performance it may expect to achieve vary from average effectiveness and low efficiency or, alternatively, average efficiency and low effectiveness. The actual outcome will be determined by the choice of goals the management of the utility decides to target. In contrast, the line labelled 'Utility C' in the diagram represents a much more capable utility, perhaps because the skills of the staff, quality of leadership and asset management systems are all excellent. Such a utility may have the capability to achieve a superior range of outcomes ranging from high effectiveness

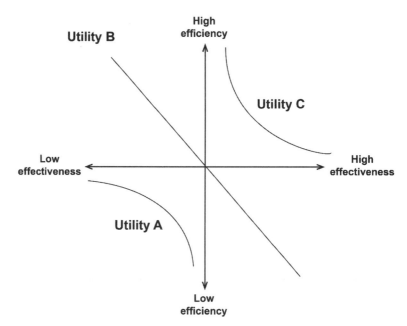

Figure 8.4 The efficiency and effectiveness mix for three different utility companies

and average efficiency to high efficiency and average effectiveness. Again, the outcomes will be determined in time by the mix of efficiency and effectiveness that is targeted.

Any ambitious utility management team will not be satisfied with the zero sum gain of trading efficiency for effectiveness to get the best mix of performance. Accordingly, the central challenge is to grow utility capabilities to allow higher levels of all types of performance to be achieved. The following three chapters will now look at the three remaining elements of the Asset Capability model – tools, organisation and teams – to explore the approaches that allow value and performance to be managed and controlled more effectively.

8.6 Conclusions

The choice of organisational **goals** is the third of the six factors included in the asset management capability model, which defines the level of asset management capability needed by a utility. In this chapter, we explored the options a utility leadership team has in selecting the appropriate mix of efficiency and effectiveness **goals**.

High effectiveness is achieved when high-quality outcomes, performance objectives and service levels are targeted. We saw that smaller utilities find effectiveness an easier **goal** to adopt and successfully deliver. This may be because smaller utilities are usually in close contact with their customers and feel an affinity with them that is harder for a large utility to achieve. High efficiency is achieved by delivering work with the minimum consumption of resources, and is typically achieved by restricting the availability of resources, such as investment and head count. In contrast, large utilities have economies of scale and supply chain benefits that allow them to achieve levels of efficiency which smaller utilities find more difficult. However, for all utilities efficiency and effectiveness are, to some degree, competing **goals**. High levels of efficiency can be achieved at the expense of some effectiveness, and vice versa.

We also saw that utility complexity makes high levels of efficiency and effectiveness difficult to achieve, and we explored several case studies where well-intended efficiency initiatives have had unfortunate side effects because the complexity of the challenge was underestimated. In one case, a well-intentioned attempt to achieve the **goal** of high efficiency in an asset management department caused minor inefficiency and threatened the effectiveness of the entire **organisation**. More sophisticated asset management systems are needed to help managers achieve the highest levels of efficiency and effectiveness.

In the next three chapters, we will explore how the choice of different **goals** can prefer different organisational structures, and how the last three factors in the asset management capability model – **tools, organisation** and **teams** – can be used to increase the effectiveness of utilities' asset management systems.

9 Asset Management Tools and Systems

9.0 Introduction

In Chapter 5 we explored the asset management capability model and its six factors. Together, these factors define the required capability of an asset management system and control the capability of any system deployed.

In Chapter 6 we reviewed how **climate**, the first in the six factors in the asset management capability model, drives the need for improved performance and a more capable asset management system.

We explored in Chapter 7 how increased utility **complexity** creates a need for a more sophisticated asset management system. We also noted that the combination of **climate** and utility **complexity** determines the required capability of a utility's asset management system.

In the previous chapter, we explored the differing and sometimes conflicting **goals** of effectiveness and efficiency. We observed that utility **complexity**, if unmanaged, can result in efficiency and effectiveness measures that clash and become ineffective.

Tools are the fourth factor in the asset management capability model and in this chapter we examine their role in enabling a utility to understand its costs and to manage value.

Utilities employ many **tools** to run their businesses. In fact, one of the major issues facing most utilities is that too many are used. This creates large amounts of unrelated data and a lack of useful information. In this chapter, we explore how the most important **tools** can be used, with particular emphasis on how these different

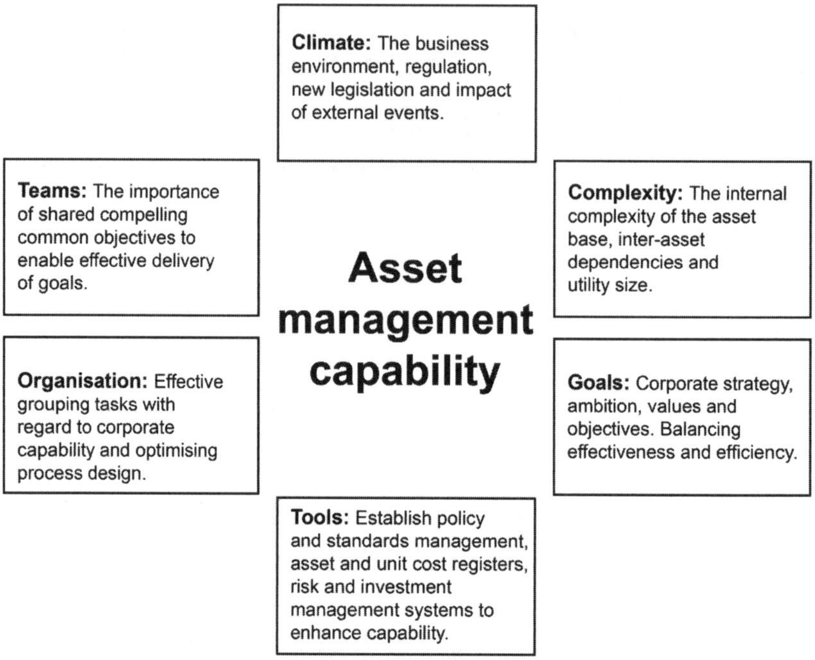

Figure 1.2 Asset management capability model

systems can be integrated, to allow value management. Only the key **tools** that are needed to create asset management capability are discussed. Commonly available information systems, whose need is self evident, such as accounts packages and programme management systems, are not explored. Every utility requires these **tools**, and a number of excellent proprietary solutions are available. The approach that enables these systems' data to be cross-referenced with other systems, however, is examined.

Figure 9.1 illustrates a schematic view of the types of tasks a utility undertakes, along with the names and chapter sections of the **tools** and approaches included in this chapter.

Two key points, which underpin the architecture of a utility's tools, to note in this figure are:

- Investment Management acts as an interface between the most strategic Level 1 utility tasks and the Level 2 tasks. In a similar fashion, Programme Management and the various

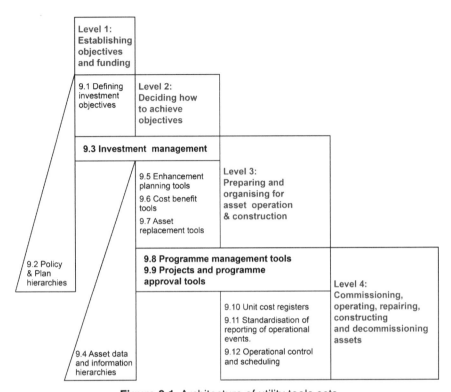

Figure 9.1 Architecture of utility tools sets

approval processes are the tools that ensure Level 2 and Level 3 tasks work together to support work delivery. Investment Management and Programme Management both prepare and maintain a single company wide view of the utilities' proposals at different levels of 'strategic-ness'. This information needs to be readily available to the many different people whose role is to plan, finance and report proposals and progress.

- Integrating all plans, principles and objectives at Levels 1 and 2 creates the need for a policy, plans and objectives hierarchy. At a less strategic level, an asset data hierarchy integrates the information used at Level 2 and Level 3 by ensuring units of work and costs for geographical areas or particular assets can be associated with each other.

In addition to helping utility staff manage value, the asset management **tools** also introduce costs and potential delay to decision-making processes. In practice, any utility needs to effectively and efficiently deploy in its own way the various **tools** discussed in this chapter. However, any one of these **tools** have the capability to enhance an organisation's effectiveness or, alternatively, bankrupt it if an over-complicated approach is pursued. Pragmatism and simplicity are essential.

As one manager commented:

"You can employ as many people as you want to change a light bulb – if that's what you want."

9.1 Defining investment objectives

Defining the short- to medium-term investment objectives for a utility and ensuring alignment with key stakeholders' expectations are of outstanding importance. Techniques that do this using objective information are particularly valuable.

For small utilities, formal price review processes are not practicable. In these situations, rate review processes agree objectives and funding. Local politicians and administrators, who are key decision makers in rate review processes, often know and employ the managers of the local utility services. As they may also have been involved in the year-to-year funding and strategic management of the service, good alignment of objectives, affordability and service targets are often possible. However year-to-year funding and budgeting is not efficient as investment plans are frequently driven by the current availability of funding, which makes efficient delivery difficult.

Conflicts of interest can also occur. On occasions, utilities find themselves obliged to provide unrelated services, such as re-surfacing municipal car parks or making specialist vehicles available for use by the fire department. One manager for a small utility commented:

"Provided the town gets its $£x m dividend each year and there are no complaints, we feel we have done a good job."

There is also a risk that any utility, small or large, which is good at responding to the needs of customers and stakeholders, can become over-responsive to short-term stakeholder objectives. Such a company may at first seem to be highly effective. However, the following case study illustrates the problems that can arise in such a situation.

Case study 1: Investing in the high-profile, rather than the highly important, work

A publicly owned electricity utility had a great ethos for providing service to its community. Each district it supplied was managed by an area operations manager who had control over budgets and workforce in that area. Economic growth and supply of first-time services to rural areas was a priority. Business leaders and local politicians strongly championed new connection projects, as a four-week delay to a new connection meant voters could not move into new houses, property developers could not sell completed schemes and new factories could not grow their work force.

This situation also suited the operational construction teams. New connections work is varied and interesting and there is a great sense of satisfaction working against a deadline to connect a new industrial estate or housing estate. But a critic could also say the lack of unit costs makes productivity management for such work difficult, and for connections work there is a greater prospect of overtime in the days preceding energisation. The company, however, genuinely valued its place in the community, its customer service and its regional role.

But all was not well. A reluctance to use contractors meant capacity was stretched, and so for six successive years programmed work to refurbish the high-voltage overhead line network was delayed repeatedly. This was of growing concern to a number of the engineers at head office. They kept designing programmes of work, and while the funding had been available for some years, delivery targets were missed. The engineers understood the risks, but every month investment plans slipped again.

Then one winter a major storm struck. The high-voltage network suffered immense damage – wood poles were blown down and tree damage meant hundreds of thousands of people lost supply; in some cases, for weeks. A significant level of economic production was lost and the press later alleged elderly people had died as a result. The long-planned high-voltage refurbishment programme was commenced that spring, but it was to take a number of years to complete and during that time, several more storms struck, followed by large outages. Customers were now angry that their long-term interests had not been managed.

Examples like this demonstrate that there is value in ensuring utilities use objective techniques to select the appropriate investment priorities.

For larger utilities, utility managers and leaders may become (or be seen to become) self-serving, or over-responsive to shareholders' need for profit. Utility managers may be accused, therefore, of excluding scope for which they have been funded, promoting the case to remove operational costs from investment funding or pursuing favoured projects. Accordingly, formal processes to determine ideal investment objectives that are beyond reproach are particularly valuable. Understanding customers' willingness to pay for services is a major step towards shaping effective asset management strategies.

The two principal types of analysis that provide these more rigorous outputs are:

- **Stated preference surveys**: The method frequently chosen by utilities[1] seeking an understanding of customers' appetite for

---

[1] US Department of Transportation's Federal Highway Administration Guide book, Publication FHWA-RD-98-166

specific services. There are two types of such research approaches possible. The first is called 'attitudinal' in which people are asked to select their choice when presented with a particular option (e.g. would they opt to take up a gas supply if one was available in their area?). Attitudinal surveys can often overestimate the response because people seem more prepared to say they will change their behaviour than they actually will. The second option is a 'hypothetical choice' survey. This technique has many advantages because it asks customers to choose between options and so the reluctance to change is common to both choices.

- **Revealed preference surveys:** These are used to observe actual behaviour, for example, trips made by household members, rather than asking respondents how they would behave in a hypothetical situation.

Hypothetical stated preference surveys are a preferred tool for understanding what services customers are willing to pay for, although these studies are often complex and expensive. For those reasons, it may only be worthwhile for utilities operating in a challenging climate or for complex utilities where internal debate makes it difficult to access the required level of detail (a cost per outcome).

This is a complex area and other issues need to be taken into account, such as prospect theory. This theory states that people are very unwilling to risk big items they already own but, nonetheless, will still happily invest small sums to play the lottery for the implausible prospect of huge reward. As a consequence quantifying customers' willingness to pay is best undertaken with a strong level of academic control over the customer research process. However strong budget control and project management by the utility is also essential and skill is needed to reconcile these issues.

An example of the results of a stated preference survey for the water industry is included in Figure 3.3 in Chapter 3.

Cost benefit tools can also be useful for accessing the value of new regulatory approaches. However, these techniques can also be used for less strategic tasks, which are discussed later.

9.2 Policy and plan hierarchies

In 2003, the 'Combined Code of Corporate Governance', which applies to companies listed on the London Stock Exchange, was issued as a consequence of the Higgs Review, an independent review that looked at the role of non-executive directors. It stated that a board's role is to:

> "...set the company's values and standards and ensure that its obligations to its shareholders and others are understood and met."

This edict reinforces the joint and personal duty that every member of the board has for the conduct of the company, regardless of title or appointment. Company boards in other parts of the world face similar obligations. Where this is the case, each board member of a utility has a duty to be sure that the board of directors both directs the management and has controls so action can be taken when necessary. These principles apply particularly to utilities in which hundreds, and often thousands, of complex projects are approved every year with little sense of how they relate to the overall direction and management of the company.

For the management and staff, who may feel they are responding to many different and contradictory issues, the challenges are different. For example, these might be:

* Working under fixed budget or head count limits to achieve certain service outcomes and efficiency targets.
* Seeking to urgently restore faults or fix busts, gas escapes and leaks with overtime restrictions.
* Working to reduce leakage while raising system pressure in areas to reduce low-pressure complaints.
* Relaxing standing rules when incidents or crises occur.
* Enacting new rules in response to an incident – although elsewhere in the organisation, news of the new rule may not have been communicated.

- Stopping or de-scoping certain practices when leaders or managers change or re-organisations occur without it being apparent a conscious decision was made to that effect. For example, one utility stopped maintaining its cathodic protection systems for large diameter steel mains and while this was clearly unwise in the absence of a design standard and a policy, the practice was tolerated for many years.
- Spending valuable time collecting asset information when there overtime restrictions and a backlog of general maintenance tasks.
- Aspiring to get the company ranked as 'number one' in its industry, but a budget cut is implemented in one area halfway through the year.

Confusion can also arise following the merger of utilities or the creation of different types of policy and standards in different parts of the business. For example, one waste water utility adopted an asset standard to require the introduction of 'fieldbus' communication protocols to aid process control and automation of sewage works. For 18 months, however, deviations to design standards were repeatedly approved by project managers who did not want parts of their projects to overspend. By the time the issue was recognised and addressed, nearly £80m of new waste water plant had been designed or built to the old communication standard.

Managing any business involves making complex trade-offs, which is why managers need to be aware of the company's principles and objectives. Building a hierarchy of policies, with a small number of managers setting direction on the most important policies and lower-level managers driving the detail needed to operate the business, will achieve this. Figure 9.2 illustrates a typical policy planning hierarchy.

The concept of a hierarchy of policy and tactical guidelines is helpful. But one challenge is language, as staff liberally use words such as 'plans', 'policy', 'strategy' and 'objectives' – simple words that can mean very different things. In the absence of clear

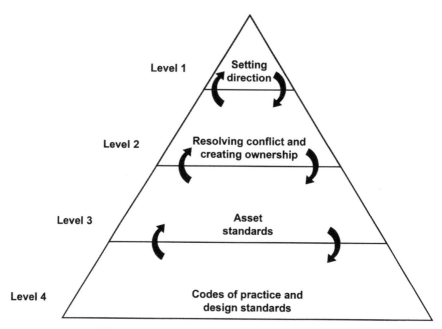

Figure 9.2 Asset Management policy hierarchy

definitions, 'policy' and 'strategy' documents have a habit of growing in complexity, which causes confusion and duplication. Almost any definition is helpful but agreeing them can be surprisingly difficult. This may be because people involved in any discussion have frequently spent a good deal of time preparing documents or guidelines in a structure they are comfortable with. Helpful guidance is included in BSI PAS 55:2008[2], which is helping to introduce common approaches in this area. Figure 9.3 suggests some additional definitions and detail for these terms.

There are also dangers in formalising company policy and standards. If the company has a conservative risk avoidance culture, there is a danger inappropriate levels of quality will be 'locked in' to work, leading to waves of unaffordable, yet policy- and standard-compliant, projects coming forward for approval. This creates major problems for senior managers. Such a situation, however, says more

---

[2] PAS 55-2:2008 prepared by the Institute of Asset Management in collaboration with BSI.

Term	Definition
Policy	A brief document detailing the principles and objectives to which the company subscribes. At Level 1 and sometimes Level 2 one page is sufficient. five and 25-year Objectives (see below) are helpful. The five year Objectives underpin current plans and are more constrained by the present. 25-year Objectives are aspirational and may require considerable stakeholder consultation before they can take root in reality.
Strategy	Small number of the most important actions and initiatives with matching Objectives which will allow delivery of Policy.
Plan	More detailed schedule of resources, outputs and costs which allows delivery of Policy, Strategy and Objectives and ensures any future failure to deliver the plan is evident. The Plans should be a subset of the corporate plan and if separate Plans are necessary their relationship to the corporate plan must be clear. (e.g.: they can be consolidated.) This ensures conflicts are identified and local ownership of Plans underpins delivery of corporate plan.
Objectives	These are the one-to five-year and possibly 25-year Objectives to which the company aims to deliver. Objectives should be specific, measurable, achievable, and realistic and time-based (SMART). High-level Objectives should be regulatory obligations, and lower level Objectives will manage value in the work delivery processes. A subset of these should be included in the score cards. High-level and low-level Objectives should be linked so that achieving low-level Objectives ensures high-level Objectives are also delivered.

Figure 9.3 Typical definitions for terms used in planning hierarchies

about the culture of the company than the effectiveness of the policies and standards themselves.

Case study 2: Examples of a hierarchy of objectives
For an electricity utility, an objectives hierarchy is very simple. At the highest level are the volumes of outputs and interventions the board needs to see delivered, linked to its regulatory contract. It may include equipment inspections, spans of tree cutting, and other high-level equipment replacement volume targets. At a lower level, more detailed outputs may be needed to ensure

projects are approved and subsequently deliver value for money and contribute to delivery of the corporate plan.

One water company manager described their system as follows:

"At the highest level (Level 1) we have the 16 regulatory objectives, which are included in our regulatory contract. The objectives are informed by our 'willingness to pay' work during a price review. We also have health and safety targets, and a range of other financial and 'people' measures. All this is held and reported in our scorecards.

"At the next level, we have a larger number of asset serviceability objectives. These are the objectives we include in project approval paperwork and maintenance planning tools, and many people have these as personal or department objectives. If the [Level 2] asset serviceability objectives are achieved, we feel we should be delivering Level 1 objectives, and so delivering the regulatory contract. The Level 2 serviceability measures include operational performance measures and it is helpful to ensure our plans support delivery [of these objectives]."

An eight-point guide for use when preparing a policy or plan hierarchy is detailed below:

1. **Simple:** Keep it simple. A good start is to make a list of the titles of the Level 1 asset management policies, get owners or groups of owners for each and establish which will need board approval. An effective Level 1 policy list should only be one page. There is no value in stating the obvious, but it is helpful to focus on areas of internal conflict. Appendix 1 gives an example of a typical Level 1 policy. By way of example Appendix 2 gives a suggested list of Level 1 policy document titles for an electricity distribution utility.

2. **Avoid duplication:** Reduce the different types of documents. In many industries, policy documents are sufficient and

individual plans could be sub-sets of the corporate plan, investment plans and programme management plans.

3. **Constrain:** Set a maximum number of Level 1 and Level 2 policies to ensure consolidation of documents, which prevents bloating their number.

4. **Speed:** Policy documents can evolve almost endlessly. Sometimes a good deal of work is necessary, particularly when issues of organisational ownership surface. Generally, most of the benefit and clarity is created in the first two drafts and the first board or leadership team review. Try to prepare first drafts of all policy documents and set review dates to tighten up on details.

5. **Budgets:** If plans containing targets and costs relating to specific Level 1 and 2 policies are prepared, their relationship to budgets and/or corporate plans should be considered. Budget owners or the corporate plan author need to be consulted. There must be clarity also on issues such as recovery of corporate overheads and pain/gain calculations on commercial contracts.

6. **Reinventing the wheel:** Most organisations already have considerable numbers of operational documents, asset standards or codes of practice. These documents can be extensive and often populate the lower tiers of the hierarchy. Include them in the hierarchy by making as few changes as possible. Renumbering, for instance, can be a much more complex task than it looks and often introduces errors.

7. **Speak the same language:** Take a bit of time to define what you mean by a plan, policy or any other terms people may use. There is no science to these definitions; any type of clarity will stop a policy sprawling into a strategy or plan.

8. **Test for completeness:** As your list of Level 1 policy subjects takes shape, a helpful challenge is to ask this question: "If we did all this, would the asset management systems have delivered an outcome that stakeholders find attractive?"

A simple and practical policy management system gives staff the confidence they are being asked to do the 'right thing' even though it may seem counter–productive to their particular roles.

> *Case study 3: Creating structure out of chaos*
>
> *Following a post-incident investigation that highlighted a number of policy document conflicts, a further review found this electricity utility had more than 500 policies and management standards in place. In total, there were seven different names for individual groups of documents and it was not clear how they all fitted together. Documents had been prepared by different departments and an earlier merger of two electricity utilities had resulted in further duplication.*
>
> *With a facilitator, the board reviewed its objectives and defined a limited number of 'statements of intent' or policies, which together gave strategic priority. Beneath this limited number of documents, further policies of a more tactical nature provided more detail on objectives and targets. The process took nine months but yielded high level and low level score-card measures. Governance processes were implemented to ensure clarity was maintained.*

9.3 Investment planning

The role of investment managers is to prepare investment plans that are subsets of the corporate plan but include details to manage value, such as information on the expenditure, regulatory outputs and benefit incentives. Comparison of this investment plan with the regulatory contract ensures the company will receive the regulatory income budgeted if the approved investment plan is delivered.

The investment plan should have sufficient detail in it to ensure the objectives and cost of work is clear. This ensures regulatory targets are achieved through a combination of investment programmes and operational responses, as the following examples illustrate:

- A combination of efficient asset replacement, regular inspection and prompt tree-cutting programmes of work maintain the faulting rate of overhead lines at a prescribed level. In addition, quick operational responses and the benefits from automated programmes reduce the time off supply once a fault has occurred. Together, these various measures define the number and length of customer outages.
- Old equipment with a greater probability of failure will also be replaced during the course of new water and waste water process plant improvements. New equipment may also give real-time asset performance information that allows greater control over processes, but requires higher levels of operating interventions (for instance, cleaning of probes and recalibrating instrumentation).
- A combination of operational initiatives focused on increasing efficiency – for instance, lowering the unit cost of a fault repair, only part of the cost of which will be charged to capital investment – extra overtime payments (to allow night time faults to be fixed more quickly) and network automation will improve service and generate incentive payments.

The growing use of regulatory incentives as well as allowances means the complex relationships between operating costs, capital investment, improvement strategies and benefit payments need to be understood. Figure 9.4 gives an extract from an investment plan for an electricity utility.

| Investment plans | Regulator agrees to make available levels of funding for investment to maintain equipment faulting rate at proscribed levels | | Regulator sets targets for allowed cost per fault repair | | Regulator agrees to make certain incentive/penalty payments if certain CML/CI (SAIDI/SAIFI) or other customer service targets are achieved |

Year by year and over the course of a regulatory period, network performance and customer service experience outcomes arise and expenditure is incurred.

| Programmes of work and real-world events | Ageing and loading of network causes fault rate to increase | Capital replacement programmes of work reduce faulting rate of equipment | Operational and control room projects and initiatives allow faults to be fixed quicker | Tree cutting reduces faulting rate of overhead networks | Street working management reduces number and impact of cable strikes | Variable impact of storms on network performance | Network automation & reinforcement investment plans reduce the impact of faults |

Note: CML/CI and SAIDI/SAIFI are terms which together define how often faults occur, how important the faults are (numbers of customers inconvenienced) and how long in total customers are off supply.

Figure 9.4 Ensuring alignment between investment plans and work programmes and strategies

9.4 Asset data and information hierarchies

As can be seen in Figure 9.5, almost half of utility executives feel the single most important issue that could improve business performance was the quality and availability of asset and unit cost data.

This figure rises to nearly 70% if respondents were asked if they felt asset data was either the most or second most important issue the business needed to address. This clearly illustrates the significance of data issues.

9.4.1 Types of asset data

The four most basic types of asset data are:

- Asset stock information. This includes the numbers, types, size and purpose of plant.
- Asset performance and condition data.
- Asset value, unit costs and refurbishment and repair costs.
- Location information, such as grid reference, post or zip code or operational zone and network connectivity.

Key improvement areas	% saying 'yes'
Are asset data improvements the principle priority for business improvement?	47%
Are departmental organisational/ teamwork issues most important?	17%
Are delivery issues most important (capex)?	30%
Are skills and succession planning most important?	7%
Total	**100%**
Proportion of utility executives who consider asset data and cost information are either the most or the second-most important business improvement issue	**67%**

Figure 9.5 Principal improvement areas that would lead to greatest business improvement

Asset stock information is held in point asset registers while location and connectivity and many network stock data (such as lengths and material types) are held in Geographical Information Systems (GIS). Both are needed and a degree of integration is necessary. That ensures the GIS holds the connectivity, location and operational boundaries of networks and plant while the Point Asset Registers hold the history and service record of particular plant, be it governors, pumps, switchgear and transformers of whole facilities, such as pumping stations or treatment works.

Utilities also often make use of a range of other major information systems. Financial system and work management systems hold critical data. For electricity and gas networks, control room systems control and manage connectivity for the higher voltages and pressures of these networks. The flow of data though these various systems requires careful planning and excellent day-to-day housekeeping.

Integration of data across systems and the business requires common data structures to be replicated in all major corporate systems. This can be achieved by creating asset hierarchies that define the relationship between 'tactical' asset information and strategic data. The concept, design and use of a 'hierarchy' and the architecture of asset data are some of the most far-reaching decisions a utility company can make to increase the effectiveness of the organisation. The next section describes some modern asset hierarchies.

9.4.2 Asset data structures and hierarchies

A key element of an effective asset data structure is the recognition of the differences between the physical asset and the purpose of that asset. The structure of an asset hierarchy defines 'locations' and the 'purpose' of the equipment. At any one point in time a pump may be sitting in that location, doing exactly what it should. It will age and be repaired, serviced, unblocked and all the time, the run time of the pump will increase. At some point, the old pump is replaced, and a new asset moves into that 'location'. However, its purpose remains unchanged.

Clear understanding of the distinction is essential as we consider data attribution and structures and where, when and how this attribution is maintained. However, it is equally as important to maintain the relationships and the history between the physical asset and its purpose, to have the ability to see the history of all assets used at a given point on the network, know all the positions where an asset has been deployed in the network and understand the work done, costs incurred and the performance of individual pieces of equipment to further support such issues as trend and root cause analysis.

To enable thorough analysis of asset information, together with effective data maintenance and collection, each asset type should be assessed to determine the correct attribution required to support meaningful analysis.

The complexity of the functional hierarchies required to support the needs of the business varies depending on the complexity of the business. In the example below, the asset hierarchy complexity is driven by the most complex of the important facility types, which in this example are waste water treatment, water treatment and sludge

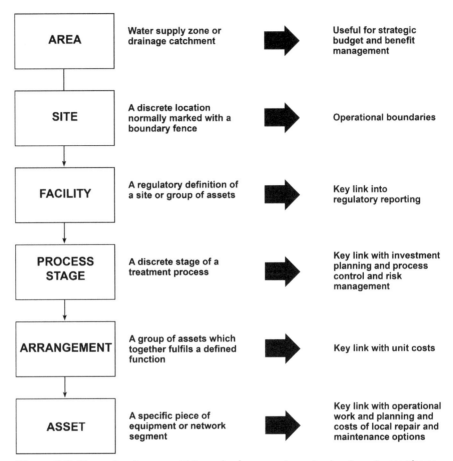

AREA	Water supply zone or drainage catchment	➡	Useful for strategic budget and benefit management
SITE	A discrete location normally marked with a boundary fence	➡	Operational boundaries
FACILITY	A regulatory definition of a site or group of assets	➡	Key link into regulatory reporting
PROCESS STAGE	A discrete stage of a treatment process	➡	Key link with investment planning and process control and risk management
ARRANGEMENT	A group of assets which together fulfils a defined function	➡	Key link with unit costs
ASSET	A specific piece of equipment or network segment	➡	Key link with operational work and planning and costs of local repair and maintenance options

Figure 9.6 Example of an asset hierarchy for a waste water treatment asset base

treatment. Many of the other 15-25 facility types typically found in water and waste water treatment utilities – such as detention tanks, boreholes and combined sewer overflows – are much simpler by nature and only make partial use of the full asset hierarchy. The hierarchy, however, must be designed to accommodate the most complex and important data structures.

The linear nature of assets in utility networks – as opposed to utility treatment processes and power generation plants, for example – means hierarchies tend to be much shallower with only a small number of layers. Additional techniques are needed to get a good view on network criticality, such as control room management systems and hydraulic modelling. Data hierarchies, however, allow strategic and tactical information about groups of assets (such as complex machinery or treatment processes) and individual assets to be stored together.

Network hierarchies typically include geographic boundaries to sub-divide the operation, such as county, local authority or postcode areas. However, the use of organisation boundaries should be avoided as they tend to be less stable and would require expensive, continual reworking of the data to maintain the alignment.

The types of issues that good data structures can resolve are many, as these examples demonstrate:

- The detailed scope of inspection, refurbishment and capital replacement work is often different. A good asset hierarchy ensures these issues are understood. For example, when work is being planned is it clear if the cost of any work needed on plinths is included in the unit cost allowance for transformer and switchgear replacement work? Alternatively, when pumps are serviced or replaced is an allowance for work on associated gearboxes included? Lastly, do contracts and work scope align with the scope of work planned? If not, there is a danger the work is unaffordable.
- The location of an asset is often critical. If it is in a duty or standby arrangement, different strategies for the same type of asset may be necessary.
- Supply chain management requires plans to be broken down into volumes of equipment, services and materials that need to be procured. If this is accommodated in the asset hierarchy, long-term plans can be translated easily into good long-term demand plans for supply chain management.

There are four simple principles that enable good data structures to be established. These are:

- **Define** an asset hierarchy, which includes definitions of the types of attributes that need to be collected. For example, if the same attributes can be used to drive asset valuations, repair costs and remaining service life, then the cost and accuracy of the data can be improved. The removal of conflicts removes the need for the creation and maintenance of conflict resolution rules. In addition, data should be collected and recorded to the level of detail that the most demanding user requires. It is possible to summarise detail for users who want less definition, but is not possible to deduce detail that is not there.

- **Use:** The data definitions need to be communicated to staff with sufficient clarity that staff can use them consistently. A degree of training is essential. If staff do not understand why this is important or the definitions are unclear, data corruption will occur.
- **Maintain:** When changes to data structures are necessary an impact assessment and a process of change control is needed. This does not have to be complex or bureaucratic. New IT systems need to be fully compliant with the company's data model or justify why they aren't.
- **Assure:** Put in place effective data quality assurance processes to assure data quality and standards.

The lack of comprehensive asset stock information, capex and opex cost data and work order or asset performance traditionally are the biggest issues for companies seeking to establish effective asset management systems. The root causes may be because managers do not understand their data requirements, or have insufficient organisational clout or fail to communicate the criticality of these issues.

Achieving a clear data model is essential and complex, and requires leadership, funding, and occasional access to some of the most experienced members of staff throughout the business. Thereafter, a continual commitment to maintenance of the model is important. A lapse of just a year in asset registration and deregistration processes will cause corruption and loss of data structure, as will the rigorous change control process for the maintenance of the data structures employed by different asset registers and models. The situation is difficult to recover without resurveying whole asset classes or regions.

9.4.3 Standardisation of asset data, information systems and business change

Local differences in how asset data is defined and recorded can make integration of records difficult. Many of these issues have arisen because, until recently, paper records had been maintained locally, each with its own set of practices.

The merging of utilities also creates complex data integration and definition issues. In one electricity utility, three operational areas still employed fundamentally different GIS systems seven years after they were 'merged' into a single business. However, each of the three operational areas was itself composed of ten separate districts that had previously had their own drawing offices and asset numbering systems. The move to single centralised data maintenance departments is a critical and challenging step on the journey towards data standardisation.

The differences in detailed data definitions become apparent and can be resolved when a new software implementation project is launched. But new large software systems can also become threats to existing data definitions. For large information systems projects initial proposals from system vendors include a significant discount if the organisation adopts the supplier's asset data model for the project, which is generally a copy from a previous and similar implementation it sold. The model is likely to be comprehensive and if a utility company's data models are not integrated and the IT project is large, then its implementation can be a good solution.

However, implementing a new data structure in one place means all the existing systems must progressively implement the same data structure. This may take years to complete and these types of collateral costs of confusion arising from large new information systems is often not recognised. Strong sponsorship of high-profile new information systems projects and poor business ownership of existing data – both of which are typical in a utility – can result in the introduction of new data models into the business, which leads to a perpetual state of confusion and costs. A clear company wide IS and data strategy and good team work are essential to resolve these issues.

Case study 4: An electricity utility seeking to upgrade its GIS (Geographical Information System) system

This utility's existing mapping system involved scanned images, but there was neither connectivity nor intelligence in the data model. In addition, better regulatory reports of numbers and duration of customer interruptions were required.

While the GIS project sought approval and later ran into technical problems, the utility's control room promoted its own solution to this particular problem. This rival solution involved extending the network control room system data model to lower voltages, which was championed by the operations director.

The control room rightly pointed out that it could refuse to energise new network developments if it did not receive high-quality 'as built' drawings from developers. This was helpful as the two data input centres, set up to reduce disruption during the move to the new system, weren't working together effectively. Operations was concerned updates were being missed, which could lead to unsafe events.

Despite the merits of this proposal, and after a review, the chief information officer realised that extending such a control room system from higher voltages down towards lower voltage levels using inferred information was extremely risky. In addition, reconciling the resulting data model with the actual location of customers would prove complex while errors in the database might not be self-evident. The prospect of a quick and cheap solution to the issue proved highly contentious and threatened to derail the GIS project several times. Ultimately, the issue was resolved by the board.

Other system conflicts that need careful management include alignment between point asset registers, line asset registers (GIS) and financial asset registers.

Gas utilities in many countries have often pioneered asset management information techniques, due to the early introduction of billing in the gas industry, retail separation, health and safety drivers, the relative simplicity of its network and its usually centralised nature. These skills and information system concepts have carried into other utility sectors because of the recruitment of gas industry staff by other utility sectors.

9.5 Enhancement (reinforcement) planning tools

Utilities must continually extend networks and add capability. Drivers for such work range from a need to address new environmental or drinking water quality standards, supply and demand issues, the need to reinforce networks to support additional load or respond to economic growth and/or climatic change.

For gas utilities, iron mains replacement work is either limited by available funding or driven by highly structured prioritisation rules. In the mature economies of North America and Europe, a range of water quality investment improvements is now largely complete and for many regions a significant proportion of the environmental sewage improvements are underway. In the Middle East, large numbers of new customers are looking to connect new load to networks. Enormous delivery and engineering challenges lay ahead as all this work is designed and integrated with existing utility networks.

These investment projects are frequently identified by regulators and specific funding for them is agreed during rate reviews or price reviews. Projects are often driven by issues such as changes in discharge consents, the introduction of new water quality standards, growing passenger volumes or electrical safety standards. Quite sophisticated tools are needed to design, scope, manage and deliver

Asset Management Tools and Systems

Flooding tools	Hydraulic and asset deterioration modelling (risk of flooding) in conjunction with terrain modelling and property categorisation (consequence of flooding).
Supply and demand of water	Rainfall modelling, network and storage models, network hydraulic models. Incidental impact of water quality issues (e.g.: arsenic, fluoride) on supply demand options. Long-term models may include customer behaviour (metering and water usage trends) and climatic change modelling.
Wastewater treatment compliance tools	Load growth, changing environmental standards, and understanding in real time the current capability of asset base. Trade effluent compliance and enforcement policy and practice.
Gas network risk management tools	Pressure and flow network management. Models tracking the impact of soil type, pipe proximity to buildings, surface type and pipe age, material and size on explosion risk to customers.
Electricity network load management tools	Load and reinforcement management, substation loading, economic and load growth and impact of faults on network management. Collateral impact of changes made in networks of different voltages which may be operated by other network owners.
Drinking water quality tools	Drinking water quality plans, real-time compliance with operational performance targets.
Sustainability and carbon management tools	Carbon management, land use, reuse of street working spoil, recycling of sewage sludge, management of oil-filled cables and use, reuse of aggressive greenhouse gasses, such as SF_6 and Biogas. CHP (Combined Heat and Power) energy planning tools.
Electricity network strategy and use plans	Introduction of distributed generation, connection of 'renewables'.
Impounding reservoir & dam risk management	Inspection and maintenance plans and programmes.

Figure 9.7 Techniques used to measure the performance and capability of utility assets

these projects. Figure 9.7 illustrates some of the techniques utilities use to measure and plan for the impact of these issues.

As these tools are well developed, tend to be industry or asset-specific and are of a technical nature, they are not discussed further. These tools support a better understanding of the nature of a problem and the type of solution appropriate. Cost benefit tools, however, are key in establishing the relative benefits of different solutions.

9.6 Cost benefit analysis tools

Cost benefit analysis tools are used to translate all costs and benefits for an investment proposal into a single ratio, typically of benefits divided by costs, after adjustment for the time value of money.

These tools are not new, and were first used in the nineteenth century by Jules Dupuit, a French economist and engineer, who was awarded the 'Légion d'honneur' in 1843 for a series of cost benefit studies on the deterioration and replacement of major Parisian road and sewage systems.

Cost benefit analysis is essential for utilities, which manage increasing numbers of conflicting non-financial benefits and penalties. For example, projects that control water-borne pollution can contribute to climate change as a consequence of carbon emissions during construction and the energy and chemicals consumed in operation over the life of the project. Such trade-offs are increasingly being considered by policy makers and utility companies. Indeed Ofwat, the economic regulator for the English and Welsh water industry, required cost benefit analysis as a central part of the PR09 price review for the 2010-2015 price review.

It is customary to calculate the ratio of benefits divided by costs. If this ratio is in excess of 1 then there is a good case for investment. The types of factors used in a cost benefit analysis include:

- Capital and operating costs
- Carbon consumed or saved (accordingly, carbon can be a benefit or a cost.)
- Loss of life, injury and illness
- Irrecoverable loss of productivity
- Traffic movements, noise and land consumption
- Environmental benefits, such as river water quality improvements and amenity enjoyment
- Service benefits.

Valuing specific benefits can be done with three different techniques. These are:

- Establishing a market price. The economic value to fishermen of fishing rights can be inferred by aggregating the fees they are prepared to pay in a season.
- Willingness to pay. This approach was reviewed earlier in this chapter.
- Benefits transfer. This approach has limitations, but if a market price has been established in a similar environment that data can be adjusted for the new situation.

The recent inclusion in cost benefit analysis of the cost of carbon emissions arising from the construction and in particular the operation of utility assets over their lifetime is resulting in some schemes being found to be unviable. The use of cost benefit analysis to establish the preferred engineering solution is generally of less value different engineering solutions frequently have similar carbon impacts. There are some exceptions to this general rule, such as projects which consider using options which make use of highly energy-intensive equipment such as incinerators.

Cost benefit analysis is a powerful technique for assessing the value of health and safety projects. In these situations a 'disproportion factor' is used to multiply the projected benefits. This has the effect of building prudence into the methodology.

Case study 5: Ofgem's use of cost benefit analysis in connection with the sale of gas distribution networks by National Grid
On 21 January 2005, Ofgem announced it approved the sale of four gas distribution networks by National Grid. A prerequisite step for this was a cost benefit analysis of the impact of this on customers.

Studies had identified that the aggregate benefits for the period 2005-2023 fell between £80m-£500 million, with a likely figure of £225m. This figure was calculated by assessing the range of outcomes that could arise from strengthened regulation of an industry composed of different network owners whose comparative performance could be measured.

In February 2006 the National Audit Office (NAO) reviewed Ofgem's methodology. While supportive of Ofgem's conclusions and methodologies, the NAO observed the restructuring costs of £100m and the future estimate of benefits were "subject to uncertainty" as it required the difference between the level of efficiencies over many future years that could be achieved with and without the sale of these networks. However, the NAO concluded Ofgem had successfully fulfilled its duties and considered the transaction had "the potential to deliver customer benefits".

The UK Health and Safety Executive (HSE) suggests a wide range of conservative principles should be used when calculating cost benefit analysis. For example, a 'disproportion factor' of 10 should be used (to reflect the aggravated unacceptability of multiple life lost from a single incident) unless a lower figure can be justified and a discount rate for future cost twice that used for benefits.

Taken together, these and other guidelines could be used by a court after an incident to consider if, with hindsight, management decisions were correct. These rules illustrate the complexity of the subject and the importance of rigour and care in preparing the cost benefit argument. For example, in complex cost benefit arguments, there is a danger that a long series of complex assumptions, which carry a systematic error, perhaps driven by optimism or pessimism, could conspire to manufacture a false or unlikely conclusion.

More recently, a number of studies of old projects have shown systematic accuracy errors have been built into past appraisals[3].

These studies show that benefits were overestimated and costs underestimated. Such issues limit the confidence with which the approach can be applied. The number of assumptions which must be made in a cost benefit analysis exercise means an objective approach to the process is essential and, whenever possible, assumptions should be verified by facts, such as willingness-to-pay studies and actual cost of projects.

9.7 Asset replacement (capital maintenance) work planning and prioritisation tools

A key tool in a utility's asset management system is the planning and prioritisation techniques that help to decide which asset replacement or maintenance projects are required. The growing cost of this type of work, its complexity and variable scope mean utility directors and economic regulators are seeking to ensure asset risk is understood, funding is sufficient and efficient, and effective mixes of capital maintenance and operating interventions are considered. The techniques that regulators use to determine the rigour of the capital maintenance asset planning systems were explored in Chapter 6.

These tools balance risk, performance and cost of different investment, maintenance, refurbishment or operation options and are of growing importance for utilities as their asset bases age. With the exceptions of waste water treatment and high-growth regions, these types of work already represent the majority of capital investment for most utility sectors.

The challenges these asset management planning tools face are two fold. Firstly, the level of funding needed throughout the next regulatory period must be agreed with the regulator and other

---

[3] Flyvberg, Holm, and Buhl, 2005 found actual rail passenger numbers was half what had been projected and previous studies had shown. In a previous study (2002) they found transport projects' costs in the sample typically were underestimated by 20%.

stakeholders. Secondly, urgent projects need to be identified and quickly delivered while ensuring sufficient funding remains for urgent and unknown projects as they arise. This leads to a need for top-down planning and bottom-up decision support tools.

- **Top-down investment planning tools**: These systems are used to prepare high-level information to construct medium- and long-term plans for the business. Incomplete data sets are accommodated and, provided systematic errors are avoided and the outcomes of assumptions are reconciled with experience, high-level long-term plans (10-25 years) can be produced.
- **Bottom-up investment prioritisation tools**: These are complex systems that inform actual investment and maintenance decisions. These tools need enormous (even by utility standards) volumes of volatile data to work well. A great deal of thought should be invested in designing and applying them to ensure they are effective and sustainable.

The top-down and bottom-up tools can be built and operated in many different ways. They are sometimes built into the same tools and processes, or held in separate systems and used by different teams of people. Although starting from different roots, both systems can be extended and developed so that their capabilities become similar.

In order to use the bottom-up prioritisation tools to generate programmes of work within the constraints of the top-down planning systems, a decision-making and reconciliation process must be undertaken. The complexity of this decision-making regime varies enormously depending on the sophistication of the top-down investment planning tools and the bottom-up prioritisation systems. Top-down and bottom-up systems and processes use 'formal' information help by the business in information systems and records of all types. The decision-making reconciliation process operating in the gap between top-down and bottom-up draws upon informal information held by the business.

A great deal of this 'informal' information will be 'know-how' and experience of experienced staff.

The distinction between top-down and bottom-up approaches is particularly significant for the more complex utility sectors, such as waste water and water treatment. This is because their complexity means it is extremely difficult for these utility sectors to ever obtain a large proportion of the asset information for all of their assets. Accordingly, such utility sectors have to make more use of complex decision-support processes to reconcile individual funding choices with overall funding constraints. In contrast, the most effective asset management systems operated by the less complex utilities, such as power generation, are reaching the point where they know nearly everything about all their assets. This allows these utilities to deploy the most comprehensive asset management systems and secure real-time control over day-to-day as well as year-to-year asset interventions across all their generating assets.

In section 5.3 in Chapter 5 we explored JR Galbraith's defining paper, 'Organisational Design: An information processing view',[4] which outlined three information strategies management teams can use to control complexity. The solution adopted by leading generation utilities is an example of Strategy 1 and the need for potentially complex decision making to quickly and affordably bridge the gap between top-down and bottom-up tools is an example of option 2. The nature of this decision-making process, which may be needed to bridge the gap between top-down and bottom-up, is also discussed below. However, the nature of these top-down and 'bottom-up tools is discussed in more detail first.

9.7.1 Top-down investment planning tools

Figure 9.8 illustrates the key components of investment planning and prioritisation models.

As companies plan for the future replacement and repair of assets, the age of the asset is the first and simplest starting point.

---

[4] Interfaces Volume 4, No 3 May 1974

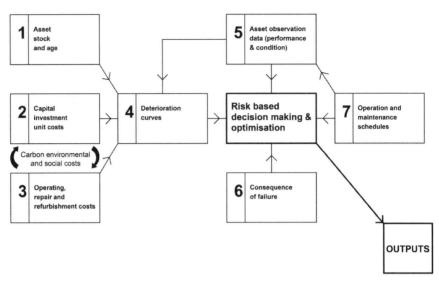

Figure 9.8 The components of investment planning and prioritisation systems

Provided the information included in boxes 1, 2, and 4 of the figure above is available, the organisation can prepare basic long-term, forward-looking capital maintenance plans. In certain cases, this might be generated by sampling known portions of the asset base, surveying it and then extrapolating the results across the full asset base.

In its simplest form, this methodology is a coarse tool that cannot 'see down' into the circumstances of particular assets and asset systems. In addition, simple top-down methodologies seek only to preserve the status quo and presume asset risk and asset performance can and should be maintained at the existing levels. As a consequence, the approach is only suited to long-term strategic investment planning. However, a benefit of the simplest types of these approaches is that because they use the smallest and simplest range of non-volatile information – age, cost and deterioration curves, all of which can be sense-checked – they are also basic and effective enough for preparing robust top-down, high-level five-year to twenty-year capital maintenance plans. The approach has several other features that are detailed below.

Advantages	Disadvantages
Robust and simple. Inputs can be audited and often tested. Great for preparing budgets and investment outcome objectives.	The methodology is only seeking to maintain the existing asset system. Impact of future changes to requirements or lack of capacity of existing assets needs to be accommodated through a separate exercise.
More accurate in the medium- and long-term for strategic investment plans where detail is not needed.	Further steps may need to be taken to identify synergies between other programmes of investment.
The process can accommodate data gaps by using samples of data.	It is too coarse a measure to identify specific investment plans and proposals.
Its simplicity means it does not 'talk up' investment projections by accumulating layers of slightly conservative assumptions to produce a bloated projection.	Care must be taken not to miss investment types, such as protection systems, office accommodation, site roads and infrastructure. For this reason top down investment plans can be underestimates.
Investment projections for different types of processes and networks are prepared within the same model and are consolidated into a single company view of investment proposals.	Simple modelling assumes operating and repair and maintenance practice continue. However, changing maintenance practices and cost inflation/efficiencies can create significant issues and options.

Avoiding systematic errors is important. If they are based on good data and take account of future strategic changes the investment plans can become forward-looking in nature.

Figure 9.9 The advantages and weaknesses of top-down investment planning tools

The application of this methodology has a number of exceptions and issues that must be taken into account. For example:

- **Assets with undetermined asset lives:** There are several types of assets for which the asset life is unclear. Examples include brick sewers (inspection and repair allows parts of the structure to be retuned towards pre-failure state) and buried low voltage cables (cables that have survived until now may be in more favourable environments).
- **The future may be different from the past:** Climatic change may change the operating temperature of networks, the

solubility of oxygen in water, the incidence of storms, the generation or use of urban air conditioning load, as well as the introduction of electric vehicles of asset management capability. Any one of these factors could be quite significant.

- **Service life extension through refurbishment and repair options**: Capital replacement is an expensive option and, in practice, the lives of assets can be extended enormously by refurbishment and repair options.

However, the majority of utility assets have an average expected service life. Local factors and events often halve or double actual service life but, nonetheless, for given levels of refurbishment and repair interventions there is an average remaining asset life for a particular type of asset. As a consequence, the thorough and comprehensive use of age-based planning systems is an effective starting point for preparing capital investment plans.

The capability of top-down investment planning decision-support tools can be extended by first including consequence analysis (box 6 in Figure 9.8) and then opex/capex/refurbishment options (box 3 in Figure 9.8). All these enhancements help close the decision-making gap between the proactive top-down investment planning tools and the reactive bottom-up prioritisation systems. Consequence analysis is particularly important for two reasons:

- **Asset replacement risk objectives**: The tracking of consequences of failure allows the risk, cost and performance of asset systems to be properly managed. This is discussed further in section 9.7.4.
- **Criticality**: In its simplest form, an assessment of consequence of failure can be used to divide assets into critical and non-critical assets. Critical assets are assets for which it is necessary to secure more asset observation data to ensure they do not fail in service, while non-critical assets are those which can be allowed to fail in service.

> *Case study 6: Reviewing failure modes and asset criticality and risk*
>
> *Pole mounted transformers supply power to houses and factories in rural and semi-rural locations across the world. They are the last transformer on the electricity distribution network prior to supply to customers. Failure of a pole-mounted transformer can result in outages and, in extreme cases, a fire inside the unit. However, they are of robust design and can operate at temperatures of up to 95° C for extended periods. Failure of the unit will only inconvenience a very small numbers of customers. Units are typically designed and rated for a lifetime of around 50 years at full rating. Most units usually operate well below the full rating, however. Consequently, the actual rate of thermal ageing of most pole-mounted transformers is much lower than that assumed in their design. In the absence of catastrophic failure events – for example, very large power surges caused by lightning strikes; or heavy corrosion of the unit over time, leading to loss of oil and subsequent loss of insulation or overheating – the units could survive for many hundreds of years. Aside from training staff to be vigilant for heavily corroded pole mounted transformers, the resilience of the equipment and the difficulty of predicting failure mean many units are run to failure.*

9.7.2 Bottom-up investment prioritisation tools

A range of increasingly complex and effective bottom-up prioritisation systems is possible. Detailed below are four such systems:

1. **Local management of events**: If budgets are delegated to the staff who actually operate and maintain the utility network there is no need for any type of system. However, in practice, such staff do not have the skills or the time to define investment proposals. In addition, large amounts of capital and project delivery resources would be required to allow all projects to be pursued, which would make this a highly

effective but extremely inefficient way of working. There is the danger that strategic issues will be overlooked, as case study 1 at the beginning of this chapter illustrated.

2. **Reactive 'problem notices':** The simplest form of bottom-up prioritisation systems is a system based on problem notices. Typically when equipment fails, a form is filled in or a call is made to the scheduling hub, where work orders and scheduling are controlled. This approach is ideal for identifying operational responses when immediate action needs to be taken. The process also identifies more complex problems, which need to be passed to a capital maintenance investment review process. At this point, the ad-hoc issue has moved into the investment decision-making gap.

3. **Reactive and structured problem notice prioritisation systems:** A number of utilities use systems that capture more information from investment work requests, which helps to establish the priority of the work in an objective manner at an earlier stage. This makes the subsequent challenge of bridging the decision-making gap between choice of individual projects and available funding much easier. That process typically involves questionnaires, which drive scoring and weighting systems of varying complexity. For simple asset systems such as networks – and particularly when specific classes of issues are being analysed, such as faults and bursts – these techniques are useful and highly effective. Training on how questionnaires should be interpreted and completed can be very helpful at getting more objective information from the operator on the scope of the issue, and the probability and impact of the relevant event. However, a number of companies operating complex processes – such as water and waste water treatment, power-generating equipment, protection and control systems – found the use of structured problem notice prioritisation systems had its own problems, as the example below illustrates.

4. **Reactive structured problem notices and cost/benefit**

> *Case study 7: Making and breaking investment prioritisation*
> *rules*
> *A water utility had introduced a prioritisation system to collect*
> *and prioritise problem notices from operations quickly.*
> *However, after 18 months, one manager commented:*
>> *"The trouble is once people get to know how the system*
>> *works; they know how to break it. For example, we*
>> *found the work programme was filling up with small*
>> *projects, which had a health and safety driver that seems*
>> *to have been exaggerated so it got to the top of the list."*
> *The company now found itself in the difficult position of*
> *having to de-scope health and safety projects from the programme.*
> *The unions immediately took an interest, and wanted proof their*
> *members' lives were not being put at risk just to save money.*

weighting: In addition to all the information collected in the previous methodology, the cost of solutions for urgent problems is estimated and a price per degree of benefit calculated. This gives a rich data set on the nature of the issue and the potential solution, while the subsequent buy order of projects is reviewed as part of the decision-making process that bridges the decision-making gap.

However, bottom-up buy lists have a habit of creating large programmes of work in strongly championed areas. At one water utility, a large number of safety projects proposed by the dam safety officer, who reported directly to a senior executive, resulted in the programme threatening to grow to three times its historic level of investment. In another company, the bottom-up prioritisation tool resulted in 80% of maintenance funding being committed after only three years (60%) of the regulatory period. A manager commented:

"All the projects were worthwhile but with hindsight, much
of that investment was poor value compared with the

schemes that were difficult to fund in the last two years of the regulatory period."

In another water company, the capital maintenance programme had become almost exclusively reactive and waste water compliance issues were growing in severity. A manager there commented:

"People became overly cautious and protected themselves with overcautious approaches. They kept asking for capital in their areas because it was what they used to have. It was hard to free up money from areas of lower priority so we could invest in the really stressed areas. However, by introducing weekly risk meetings we could allocate capital [and project delivery resources] to those parts of our waste water business where the greatest priorities existed."

These issues arose not because of problems with bottom-up prioritisation and scheduling systems. Sensibly prioritised lists of worthwhile projects, addressing different types of problems, were undoubtedly prepared in certain areas. But some managers will always be more skilful at promoting their projects and this makes the decision-making systems seeking to identify the best projects and so to bridge the gap between bottom-up requests and top-down constraints harder to operate.

9.3.7 Bridging the decision-making gap between top-down and bottom-up decision support tools

By developing increasingly sophisticated top-down and bottom-up decision-support tools the gap between them is increasingly narrowed. Figure 9.10 uses the numbering system referred to in the components included in Figure 9.8, and illustrates how utilities can make investment decision making quicker, easier and more objective.

As the decision-making gap between top-down and bottom-up tools closes, complexity moves from the flexible and often expert informed processes that operate in the gap, into the more formalised

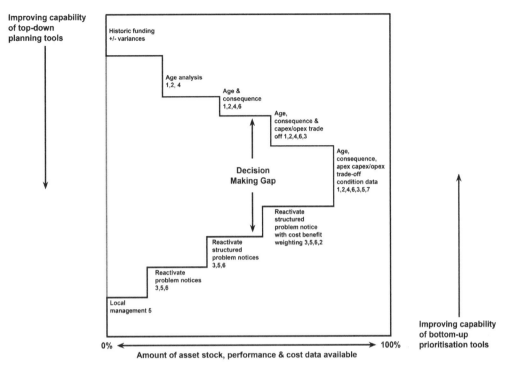

Figure 9.10 Illustrating how the growing capability of decision-support tools can close the decision-making gap

top-down and bottom-up processes. If done well, this leads to substantial efficiency and effectiveness benefits. However, attempts to mechanise highly complex or chaotic asset systems with insufficient information are not possible, even though an answer will always be produced. The range of approaches that can be used to bridge the gap can be categorised into four types, each of which is discussed below.

Type 1: Budget constrained local decision making

In this case, budgets are allocated to quite localised operational areas to allow operational staff to undertake interventions. Operators have all the information and funding on the issues that need resolution. There is often a strong call from operators for more capital investment and great resistance to giving up budget that has been previously allowed. Too much capital is inefficient and too little results in operational staff feeling they are unaccountable for day-to-day performance. Accordingly,

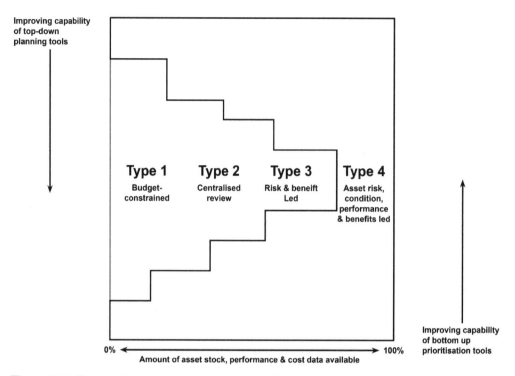

Figure 9.11 Bridging the decision making gap and the four types of decision-support processes

processes are needed to challenge budget levels from time to time. These processes generally involve annual or six-monthly reviews to establish if the budgets for this type of work were too big or not big enough. These reviews can become contentious, which makes high levels of organisational clarity and team working even more important. These issues will be explored in Chapters 10 and 11.

Type 2: Centralised review

In this case, a central team reviews proposals. This may involve commissioning studies to explore issues raised and defining appropriate solutions. To assist these studies, typical bottom-up tools ensure breakdown reports on the past history of processes and equipment available, while one-off asset surveys reveal the condition and performance of troublesome plant and equipment. This provides a view on the probabilities and consequences of future equipment failures. Named individuals own programmes and sub-programmes of investment options, which are prioritised. Affordable projects are determined by using programme budgets to establish cut lines on programmes of work. Investment benefits are optimised by comparing the merits of projects with those in different programmes of work that are unaffordable. This allows programme budgets to be flexed and optimises value for money.

Type 3: Risk and benefit led
In addition to all the features of Type 2 above, additional rigour and review processes have been used by leading companies to inject more objectivity into complex investment appraisal decision-making processes. Several themes are common to these approaches:

- **Clock speed:** Regular (weekly, fortnightly) risk reviews are greatly valued by operations staff, who feel confident that their concerns are dealt with urgently. This gives the process credibility. In times of crisis or change, this approach is used by asset management/investment planning leaders to encourage their staff to move quickly to an investment decision.
- **Central costing:** Costs of solutions are often prepared by central teams to ensure objectivity. This is important as investment decisions are made in the early stages of a project or programme of work. (Proposals may only be at the 'Needs' or 'Initiation' phase as defined in Figure 9.17, which will be discussed in section 9.9 and normal work-pricing techniques are not applicable.
- **Structure and language:** Several companies invested in extensive risk training and investment planning for groups of operational staff to ensure a common language, clarify the concepts of probability, risk, problems and consequences and agree common definitions and yardsticks.
- **Behaviours:** Involving operations in these reviews is critical. But with this involvement comes a responsibility that Operational staff resist the temptation to present their case

until investment is approved. Two companies mentioned their panels approved investment projects that appeared to be worthwhile even though they did not satisfy the formal risk appraisal model criteria. The review panels were composed of experienced business people who looked at investment issues on their merits, using the company-approved risk assessment methodologies as guidance. One manager said:

"We wanted people to know it is us who are managing the business and not our business rules. That encourages people to come to the reviews with the expectation there will be a real debate of the issues."

This ensured project sponsors had the confidence to present their proposals in a business-like manner, and not go to great lengths to simply tick all the right boxes.

- **What next:** One company recognised that the decision not to invest might be the end of the investment appraisal process but it still meant someone was left with a problem that needed resolution. Accordingly, the meeting would then explore what help could be made available to overcome the issue. Operational staff, in particular, found this empowering.

Type 4: Asset risk, condition, performance and benefits lead planning and prioritisation systems

By recording the location, condition and performance of all utility assets, the benefits of the top-down and bottom-up methodologies can be combined. As 'bottom-up' information consists of information on day to day events such systems allow the seamless integration of day to day operational events and long term investment planning. However, operational performance and asset observation data collection and maintenance is expensive. It is also difficult to do effectively and the lack of rigorously defined asset condition and performance measures may result in the collection of asset observation data that is inconsistent or subjective, as the following case study illustrates.

Case study 8: Collecting long-term asset observation data
An electricity distribution utility developed a process to collect improved condition data on substation infrastructure. This was important not only to prevent the public from breaking into warm dry substations, but also to ensure the utility could prove it had taken all reasonable measures to prevent people from doing so.

A system was adopted which used six gradations of asset deterioration, with grade one being new and six being very severe dilapidation. After a sample of 500 substations had been inspected, a review indicated there were two issues. Firstly, the size of the investment programme if grade four work was included could not be justified, yet there were urgent door repairs required for some grade four substations. Accordingly, definitions were amended to move to an eight-grade system. Secondly, there were variations in the results between the three surveyors who were undertaking the inspections. For commercial reasons, a proposal was introduced to use one surveyor to review the entire stock of substations and secure the appropriate level of consistency. However, the inconsistency was also due to lack of clarity of the grade definitions, which meant operational staff could not complete surveys during routine maintenance, nor would it be possible to generate deterioration curves. Sets of photographs were included in the inspection packs to clarify definitions. The system was successfully implemented.

Figure 9.12 illustrates a process for generating asset information and prioritisation processes, which can be used to prioritise investment effectively.

A variety of asset observations are now used by utilities to predict the remaining life of their assets. Figure 9.13 lists examples of the observations, which give a good indication of the remaining life of particular assets.

The major benefit of an effective capital investment prioritisation system is the clarity over asset cost, risk and performance. This shared and objective clarity is of enormous value to operational,

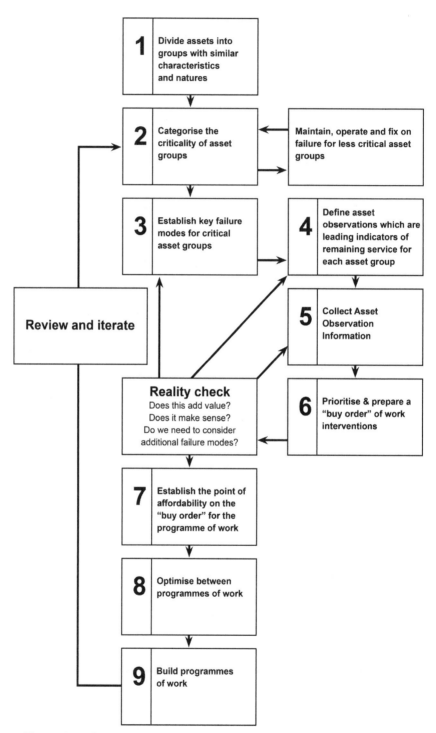

Figure 9.12 Prioritisation process for building effective programmes of work

Asset type	Asset observation
Civil structures	Defect surveys, ground movement tracking.
Transformers	Loading, manufacturer, service history including oil sample analysis history, noise.
Pumps	Type (manufacturer and model number), material pumped, hours run time, peak loading events, acoustic monitoring data, pump control system, blockage history.
HV overhead power lines	Weakest wood pole, proximity of trees and branches, future peak wind speed, materials of construction (conductor), propensity for ice loading, width of cross arms, criticality and availability of auto re-closers.
General equipment, cabinets exposed to the environment and towers	Paint condition, proximity to the sea, freeze-thaw events, temperature precipitation and exposure to road salt spray.
Sub-station Infrastructure, Doors and Switchgear Enclosures	Age and condition of woodwork. Effective operation of locks and closures, risk of vandalism by post code.
Water Networks	Material of construction, water hardness/softness, pressure, freeze thaw events, burst history, soil type, diameter.
Gas Mains	Material of construction, pressure, service record, proximity to buildings, surface type and ground conditions, cathodic protection type, history of 'town' and natural gas.
Gravity Sewers - Blockage	Blockage records, CCTV condition inspection records, last de-silting operation, construction material, diameter, age, population type, gradient.
Gravity Sewers - Collapse	Traffic loading, soil type, collapse & blockage records, CCTV condition inspection records, construction material, diameter, age, surcharge frequency.

Figure 9.13 Examples of asset observations that can be used to predict remaining service life for a range of utility assets

planning and regulatory managers and utility regulators. However, for a well-run and sensibly funded utility, deferring investment until it is needed produces efficiencies. In addition to temporarily saving the cost of investment, deferring replacement work also means assets with remaining service life are not scrapped prematurely. Operating safely by better understanding the risks adds value, as seen in the following case study.

Case study 9: Managing asset risk with asset condition data

In addition to responding to urgent network issues reactively electricity distribution companies also design proactive asset replacement programmes which maintain network resilience. For one electricity utility its £60m a year overhead line asset replacement programme involved the detailed inspection and refurbishment each year of one fifteenth of the network. Accordingly over a fifteen year period the whole network would have received preventative maintenance and the cycle could repeat itself. Work was undertaken up to a high standard. In order to better control over scope and risk of the proactive asset replacement programme a condition data capture programme for the entire network was launched.

By using a wireless data capture system the company collected condition data on the companies' 11,000km of 33kv, high voltage and low voltage overhead lines. The total cost of the exercise was £2m and took 26 months to plan and undertake.

Analysis of the condition data revealed the following issues:

1. *A much greater number of safety issues arising from ground clearance issues[5] and a large number of safety issues associated with clearances from buildings and objects became apparent.*
2. *Certain safety issues relating to bare conductor services were identified as particularly pressing and more suited to efficient and quick delivery by a dedicated programme of work.*
3. *A number of stays[6] which did not have insulators as will be required by statute from January 2013 and stay insulators of an older type where replacement is required.*
4. *Safety issues relating to wood-poles[7] where the factor of safety had deteriorated to levels where replacement was required because of wood rot, bird (woodpecker) damage etc.*

5. *The improved asset information gave the company the capability of deferring less urgent asset replacement work in a controlled manner.*

A five year programme of asset replacement work for the entire network was assembled. In doing so detailed refurbishment specifications were prepared for the 15,000 maintenance units on the network which needed some attention. In practice this meant that over this five year period some work (which represented the most critical work) would be undertaken on three quarters of the network. The detailed condition information meant non critical work (generally work which raised asset condition to level 2-4 in the asset health index) could be deferred with confidence and addressed in five year's time. The extra asset information allowed more detailed programme planning. By making distinctions between work that can be carried out with the lines live and dead, projects were allocated to separate regional programmes of work and more efficient ways of working were established. In addition detailed and highly specific scopes were given to contractors. This meant the utility had better control over scope, cost and asset risk. Accordingly the types of issues discussed in case study 1 in chapter 7 were addressed. The cost of the condition data survey was nearly £2m. During that time operational staff continually queried if it was worthwhile spending months collecting as many as 42 bits of information about individual bits of equipment when:

"Anyone with eyes in their head can see what needs to be done".

The data allowed a change in management policy to address the pressing issues in a timely and efficient manner and at a reduced cost to usual business practice. Other currently less critical work may be picked up in due course - following a future

review of investment policy which again will be informed by
renewed detailed condition data.

[5] In general terms 'ground clearances' refer to minimum distances laid down
in statute for the distance between a conductor and ground at a given
operating voltage. Clearances from buildings and objects refer to minimum
distances between conductors and buildings or other fixed objects which are
set out in the industry's national standards and are now referenced in statute.
The minimum clearances specified are dependant on voltage and the
accessibility of the part of the building or object from which they are
measured.

[6] Stays are wire supports which give power line wood poles support but
create a risk of electrification.

[7] Wood poles hold up overhead power lines and telephone lines. If poorly
managed, they are vulnerable to large-scale failure in storm conditions, high
levels of network failure and extended outages for customers.

9.7.4 Managing asset risk, cost and performance

The performance of the utility system is driven by the cumulative
impact of equipment failures and other events that degrade
performance. We looked earlier in Figure 9.8 at prioritisation
processes driven by asset observation data and deterioration curves,
which estimate the remaining service life of large numbers of
different assets objectively. For the proactive management of complex
asset systems, however, it is helpful to value the consequences of
particular asset failures and different levels of performance.
Investment plans can therefore be made of all the interventions that
most efficiently deliver the affordable level of performance. Each of
these issues is discussed below.

Valuing required performance levels: In some sectors, contract or
regulatory mechanisms place a value on certain levels of
performance. This information places a value on small changes in
customer service, and so establishes the maximum cost a customer
might be expected to pay for service improvement.

In the electricity industry, for example, the cost per minute of
supply lost to a customer and the cost per interruption to supply are
specified. In the rail sector, comprehensive metrics are sometimes

included in contract documentation at the information centre used to measure the availability of passenger capacity at different times of the day, availability of escalators and lifts, the customer service experience and the ambience of stations and public places. In the power generation sector, the availability of traded power also places a value on lost generating capacity, which is helpful in quantifying the type of economically efficient performance needed.

In addition, willingness-to-pay studies, which were discussed earlier, are very helpful in establishing the value of certain performance levels. Before using this information, however, it should be noted that, in practice, it is very difficult to justify any decline in service. Accordingly, asset replacement levels in electricity distribution are driven by a need to contain the faulting rate of the network. Figure 9.14, which is reproduced with the kind permission of Electricity North West, illustrates an asset health methodology used by the electricity industry to identify asset replacement strategies for 11kv circuit breakers.

Valuing the consequences of individual asset failures: For the most complex utilities, such as water and waste water, consequence modelling is necessary to understand how equipment failures will

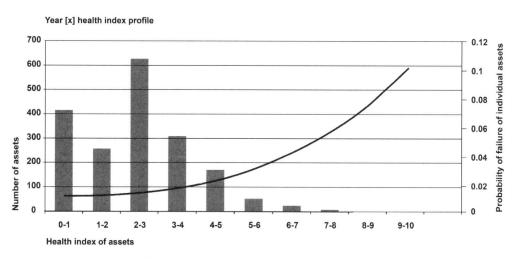

Figure 9.14 Asset health projections for ENW

affect customer service. In Figure 9.6, we examined an asset hierarchy and noted that regulatory reporting is undertaken for individual facilities, such as pumping stations.

Accordingly, it is necessary to model how facility service performance is degraded by the failure and repair of individual assets. This requires an understanding of the impact an asset failure has on an arrangement of machinery, and the consequences of service failure an arrangement has on a process stage, and, lastly, the impact that process performance has on overall facility performance.

This is important because the existence of parallel treatment streams and standby equipment significantly reduces the impact of individual assets or processes. For the largest and most complex facilities, such as sludge treatment or larger water or waste water treatment plants, drawing up site-specific models is worthwhile. For most facility types, however, it is reasonable to assume a generic process facility and process model for a particular facility type, which is driven by asset information (such as the number and size of different treatment streams) to reflect the criticality of individual assets.

With these models, information on the likelihood of asset failure, run time before repair, and the cost and performance of temporary measures can be used for hundreds, and sometimes thousands, of individual facilities to predict service degradation. Figure 9.15, which is reproduced with the kind permission of United Utilities, illustrates the output from such a model for a range of waste water treatment plans.

In Figure 9.15, the service measures to the right of the diagram are the quality measures that define the effectiveness of the treatment process. These serviceability measures are the Level 2 objectives explored in the policy and plan hierarchy structures discussed earlier in this chapter in case study 2. This ensures the Level 1 objectives (willingness-to-pay constraints and high-level regulatory targets) will be achieved as a consequence of investment plan delivery.

In developing and using these tools there are two practical points to note:

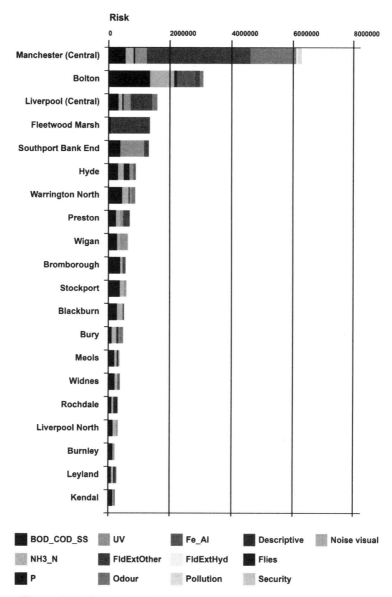

Figure 9.15 Serviceability predictions for waste water treatment works

- **Constrain predictions by observed facts:** The complexity of these models means there is a danger large numbers of assumptions will conspire to create distorted outputs. For this reason, predictions must be validated by real observations. Even though asset observation data means the service life of a type of asset may vary, the actual asset life or intervention frequency should equal the average age of assets that are replaced. Process and facility models can then be checked for credibility by comparing actual service degradation with predicted performance for specific facilities, so adjustments can be made if necessary.

- **Understand what level of detail is 'real':** At a strategic level, these models share the characteristic of the simplest top-down, asset planning tools and give good high-level, short- and long-term plans. The models predict the service outcomes from individual asset failures at any point over the next twenty five years. However, these are predictions of the most likely events and, at some point, the detail itself becomes unreliable. This is because no model can ever take account of all the potential variables. It is important these limitations are understood. These are decision support tools so if users, board directors and regulators believe these systems will predict specific events in the future, it is likely they will be disappointed and confidence in the tool undermined. If there is a good business case, improved data – such as real-time asset performance data – can be used to manage risk and individual asset events. Indeed, these techniques are being used in aerospace and power generation plant. These approaches are costly, however, and are only applicable to the most critical assets and systems.

9.7.5 The need to use the right mix of proactive and reactive planning tools and decision-making processes

In theory, the use of the above techniques could be used to close the decision-making gap for quite complex utilities. To do so, asset hierarchies that categorised assets into many thousands of specific asset types would be needed, as would large quantities of data on the failure modes of each asset type. For the more complex utility industries, such as waste water or water, it is extremely difficult to close the decision-making gap with formal processes and tools. In many cases, the assets cannot be inspected at will, real-time performance data may not be available and, as was observed in Chapter 7, the chaotic nature of biological treatment systems makes 100% modelling impractical.

Accordingly, short-term budget setting with due regard to historic levels of spend and local management of activity (area on the left of Figure 9.10) and Type 1 budget-constrained decision making (Figure 9.11) are practical and appropriate for stable, non-critical assets. Conversely, critical assets that can be easily and cheaply inspected – such as railway track, road surfaces or overhead power lines – benefit from Type 4 asset risk, condition and performance and benefits led processes. However, all these tools are decision-support tools, and need to be used by experienced people to help them make better decisions quicker.

9.8 Programme management tools

Programme management is a central function, which provides the business with objective information on the progress, current and future costs and governance of projects. There are a number of excellent proprietary databases and systems that enable a utility to record and manage programmes of work. These systems are not discussed here, although several methods of using them to improve their rigour are.

Programme management is a great skill and very different in culture from project management. The challenge for a programme manager is to anticipate and plan for the outcome of all the projects in the investment portfolio.

Considerable work over time has shown people are consistently optimistic in the early stage of projects. This is reflected in the United Kingdom's Treasury Green book[7] (*www.hm-treasury.gov.uk/data_greenbook_business.htm*), which observes:

---

[7] Subject to Crown Copyright

"Within the public and private sectors, there is a demonstrated and systematic tendency for project appraisers to be overly optimistic. This is a worldwide phenomenon, whereby appraisers tend to overstate benefits and underestimate timings and costs, both capital and operational."

The scale of this systemic tendency is significant with figures of up to 66%[8] observed. This situation creates challenges for programme managers who need to identify unfunded costs early and distinguish between those projects that hold both appropriate and excessive contingency.

There can be times when programme management reports unwelcome news, so experienced and respected staff and broad sponsorship of the function are essential. When this process breaks down, which it can very easily do, it is common for several people to attend the same meeting with their own figures seeking to explain their view of what is going on. All the figures are generally correct, although they may differ due to timing and assumptions around overheads and costs. This will lead to a delay in corrective action while the reasons for the differing figures are investigated.

The strategic significance of this area was seen earlier in Figure 9.5, which noted that 30% of utility executives felt better control over work delivery was the most important improvement area for performance in their utility. The companies that give this subject the greatest priority for improvement broadly split into three groups where the drivers for change and improvement were:

1. **Accelerate delivery capability:** Increase capacity to deliver targeted investment. All these companies consistently delivered less than a third of the budgeted capital investment improvements. In each case, the company managed both

[8] Page 50, Public Sector Business Cases using the Five Case Model: a Toolkit, United Kingdom's Treasury Green book. Subject to Crown Copyright

challenging programmes of high-profile work with stakeholders who closely monitored delivery progress.

2. **Get greater efficiency**: These companies targeted greater capital efficiency from the large numbers of smaller projects that made up their capital investment programmes.

3. **Getting the right scope delivered:** For these businesses, the focus was to ensure the most important work (as opposed to the less complex or easier-to-deliver scope) was delivered first.

The symptoms of poor programme management include:

- A lack of shared understanding of the most likely out-turn costs or projects and programmes.

- Projects and programmes of work that hold their own excess levels of contingency, and which result in a 'bow wave' of spend expected in the next two to four months, which never occurs. In stable conditions and in the absence of good programme management, actual levels of spend are invariably a great deal less than was predicted a year before. These lower levels of spending are often attributed to a mix of slippage (which is bad) and release of unspent contingency (which is welcome). Differentiating between these issues is critical. This can be undertaken by looking at changes in short-term spend for projects and cross-referencing this spend change with any change in the out-turn costs for the project, and aggregating the individual project issues to create programme reports. As a consequence, poor cost reporting and housekeeping from individual projects shroud the results of analysis in uncertainty. The degree of under-spending can vary depending on the complexity and character of projects. Programmes of complex IT and water and waste water treatment projects can experience slippage of 10-25% from year to year. Higher voltage reinforcement projects exhibit this tendency to slip but the criticality of outages means such slippage is often unacceptable. A skilful programme management function will seek to anticipate and identify these trends.

- Project managers bailing out of difficult projects.
- Errors in consolidating the cost of different programmes of work. Particular areas of challenge include overheads and central costs which are applied to different programmes in different ways from financial year to financial year.
- Project managers are not able to exert control over their projects, because:
  - Others can book costs or cost over-runs to the projects with impunity
  - Project managers do not have access to the operational resources and craftsmen needed
  - The scope was not tightly defined at the outset, but undocumented scope growth occurs during delivery as these details are clarified.

For major projects in the utility sector, dedicated and experienced project managers are invariably accountable for project costs. Particular challenges exist for the many thousands of smaller projects. For projects of less than £50,000 in value, traditional project management disciplines can be impractical and more reliance on personal oversight and sponsorship is necessary. A backward-looking test of project governance is detailed below.

Case study 10: Investment programme health check
An electricity utility examined the predicted out-turn cost of all very mature or recently completed projects. Figure 9.16 was produced by calculating the ratio between out-turn cost and approval cost for each project, and plotting the cumulative frequency of those ratios.

This showed that nearly 32% of all projects either spend up to project approval value and a further 8% spent up to project

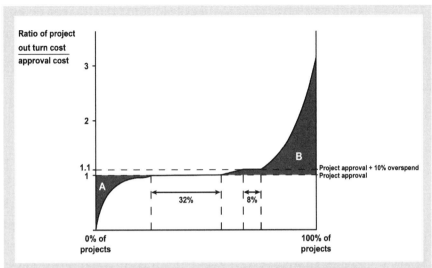

Figure 9.16 Exploring the effectiveness of project management governance

approval value plus contingency. This implies a culture of 'can spend' rather than 'must spend' and a review of project governance and project management was initiated. In addition, area A on the graph represents the aggregate underspend of projects, while area B, which is twice the size of A, represents the total overspending of projects above initial approval. Further work revealed some projects had started four years previously so inflation of labour and materials swelled out-turn costs. This work led to the development of medium-term key performance indicators to review the programme's health, and an annual review.

In the gas and electricity distribution sectors, key craftsmen – such as overhead linesman, fitters and jointers – are needed for day-to-day fault and/or gas escape repairs. These same people, however, are also needed for capital and mains replacement project delivery and switching operations. This can makes the role of the project manager particularly difficult, as they have to draw on resources that report to managers contending with their own day-to-day operational issues. This conflict can undermine the effectiveness and authority of project managers and make efficient delivery difficult. This has implications for organisational design, which is discussed further in Chapter 11.

9.9 Project and programme approval tools

The investment approval processes in any utility are key. So far we have explored how the various tools listed in Figure 9.7 and the bottom-up and top-down asset replacement tools can establish the need for a particular investment project. However, as projects and programmes of work mature, the involvement of construction and design engineers and operational staff quickly becomes central. If these staff have not been involved in the project from the outset, it is extremely difficult for them to take ownership for cost and scope and deliver work once projects are approved.

Once the scope and solution of the problem are clear, the project or programme must be fully handed over to the design and delivery organisation. Considerable investment into detailed design, route proving, land purchase and planning issues will also occur. This handover is a critical process and discussions with utility companies highlight the fact it often doesn't work well.

One of the most important requests from construction and delivery teams in most utilities is early visibility of projects and programmes of work. Invariably, these staff complain of late approval of work, which doesn't allow sufficient time for efficient delivery. In part, this situation arises because the complexity and slow pace of price reviews, extra land planning, access issues and environmental studies leave less time for scheme delivery. Most utilities, however, also have scope to increase the efficiency and speed of their internal decision-making processes.

Case study 11: Don't shoot the messenger
One recently recruited senior executive at a water utility observed that many projects were caught in long cycles of optioneering – to

the extent that the entire allowance for some projects had been spent in considering as many as ten different project solutions. Project staff continually looked for new solutions to problems because they could, and because it could result in some additional savings. There didn't seem to be a push to make difficult decisions, so more study and more optioneering seemed like the right and comfortable choice. When staff in asset management and construction were asked to suggest why this had come about, there were two explanations that featured often:

1. *Lack of clarity of the process: The approval process seemed an opportunity for finance people to ask really detailed questions about schemes and find fault with them. In some instances, previous decisions or approvals were reversed.*
2. *Senior management do not like the answer: Projects for which an insufficient allowance had been agreed with the regulator were repeatedly refused approval by senior managers and directors. Optioneering continued with increasingly unlikely options considered in the hope an ideal solution would suddenly appear.*

Key steps to accelerate decision making are to avoid duplication and get clarity on the approval process. Figure 9.17 includes definitions of project or programme maturity that can be used to establish objective but generic project milestones for projects under consideration.

For smaller projects, a number of the early approval stages may be minor administrative tasks for managers, who simply need to track progress and keep a one-page baseline summary of the decisions. For network projects, some of the earlier stages, such as initiation, may not be worthwhile. Some of the organisational and process issues relating to this are developed further in the next chapter.

Milestone	Needs approval	Initiation approval	Scope and solution approval	Financial approval
What does this approval mean?	- We have decided there is an issue which needs resolution but we may be unclear of the scale or nature. - The initiation stage of the project has started.	- We are ready to spend an approved budget deciding on the best type of solution. - The scope and solution stage of the project has started.	- We know what we need to achieve and the type of solution we will use. - Focus moves on to detailed design and planning for delivery.	- We are clear the project is affordable, needed and we have resolved to deliver it. - Focus moves on to Procurement and Delivery.
Approval criteria	- The timescale and budget for the needs study is sufficiently clear. - The objectives of the initiation study are reasonably clear. - The sponsor and person/ organisation doing the initiation study are clear.	- We understand the underlying nature and scale of the issue. - We understand out turn costs reasonably. - The issue is pressing and we believe it is good value. - We have a funding provision in the programme for this type of work. - We understand the benefits, objectives and a list of options to be considered and we know when we need it. - Projects are grouped together into the largest practicable package. These may become programmes of work. - Whole life project manager and whole life sponsor appointed. Network of participants ('NOP' or key 'stakeholders') appointed and led by project manager.	- All options and objectives detailed in Initiation Statement have been considered and accommodated. - The engineering solution is safe, proper and reasonably tested. - Proposals satisfy relevant standards and policies. - All outages and interdependencies are identified and we believe will be resolved with a reasonable degree of confidence by a date. - Opex/Capex/Repex/Customer issues are in balance. - On approval we understand the cost to +/-30% with 80% confidence. - key stakeholders have agreed the solution.	- All scope and solution decisions are satisfied and remain valid. - We have funding identified in the programme for this work. - Contingencies (where possible named contingencies) exist for outstanding issues. Value of contingencies unlikely to exceed 10% of project approval value. - On financial approval we know costs to +/-10% with 80% certainty. (i.e. we expect 1 in 10 projects to end up costing more than 10% of approved funding and 1 in 10 projects to under spend by 10%).
Programme quality checks & reviews	- Templates are in place which ensures 'needs approval' is not over- or under-bureaucratic. - Volumes of work in 'needs' stage is tracked and controlled. - Aggregate cost of 'needs' studies tracked.	- Cost of 'Initiation' work as a proportion of Financial Approval. Tracked. - On average initiation approval budgets are reasonably accurate compared with final approvals (6 month rolling average). - It is unusual for scope and solution reviews to consider options which were not identified at Initiation approval.	- Project managers and sponsors are of correct level of seniority so that they have authority and knowledge of project issues. - There is no major systematic under costing of scope and solution proposals. - It is unusual for more than 1 in 10 projects to receive financial approval at more than 30% above scope and solution approval cost).	- Change requests for deviations from scope and solution approvals not too common. - As many projects overspend as underspend. - Reworking of scope and solution work is rare. - Aggregate value of work in progress locked up at each approval stage tracked.

Figure 9.17 Project and programme maturity milestones

9.10   Unit cost registers

Consolidating a company's various views on the cost of work is complex but necessary if effective high-level plans are to be prepared for the operational and capital construction teams to use without renegotiation or reinterpretation. In addition, easy translation of investment plans into robust medium- and short-term demand plans that can be used for supply chain management will yield substantial efficiencies.

> *Case study 12: Internal re-negotiation of the investment plan*
> *An electricity network operator completed and agreed the scope of its reinforcement programme with its regulator as part of a rate/regulatory review. However, when the plan was handed over to the delivery organisation, key influential project managers complained there was insufficient funding for the projects. A long discussion started, and project managers cited individual examples of the unclear scope of projects, unfunded commodity inflation and scope challenge.*
>
> *It was not clear what the relative significance of each of those factors was as the investment plans had been priced using high-level units of work and project managers were pricing up their view of what was needed given local conditions. The project delivery teams also asked the investment planning teams questions that they could not answer, such as where the allowance for collateral works needed for protection systems or enabling works were. In addition to delaying commencement of delivery for six months, this resulted in the review of the entire programme, which was re-planned with scope moving between projects to make delivery more efficient. Towards the end of the price review, only two of the largest 26 schemes completed bore a close agreement to the pro-forma scope that had been agreed initially. This created a good deal of additional risk and review work for the utility and the regulator.*

The levels at which units of work are valued by the unit cost systems need to be carefully specified. An example of how an asset hierarchy can be used to accommodate different data sets was illustrated in Figure 9.6. In this example, the groups of assets at arrangement level can be valued using the unit cost register. This is practical as construction design and construction delivery can work with this type of assets collection.

Accordingly, the cost or arrangement and the numbers of arrangements can be multiplied to create asset inventories and indicate replacement costs. In contrast, operational staff fix, inspect and repair individual assets but the cost and scheduling of work are managed and planned at asset level. If these types of issues are not carefully thought through, ways of working and information systems will fragment. Different teams will be using different information and whole life decisions are impossible.

The data architecture must be designed and agreed by a broad team composed of operational, capital construction, supply chain management and asset planning staff.

Examples of the areas where utilities experience problems in establishing cost registers are:

- The complexity of the project was underestimated.
- Definitions of units of work were not resolved at the outset.
- Suppliers and construction partners were unwilling to disclose actual costs for commercial reasons.
- Tenders and contracts for work were specified in ways that made desegregation of out-turn costs difficult.
- Overly complex solutions were attempted without checking what costs and effort would be required to complete the work.
- The unit cost of smaller items of work weren't agreed at the outset to establish the treatment of programme level 'pain/gain' mechanisms.
- Units of work weren't defined to accommodate all users of the data. Asset planners typically only want indicative prices

for groups of assets. Supply chain managers need to understand volumes of specific types of equipment and materials that will be procured. Construction teams manage contracts and development phases.

- The division of work into different groups wasn't decided in detail at the outset. The method of delivery of work determines unit costs. Different unit costs and overheads may apply to smaller and larger projects.

- The level at which carbon accounting is introduced wasn't decided early and was too complex. The introduction of carbon accounting requires an understanding of the quantities of commodities included in different types of construction work. However, the biggest driver of carbon generation from equipment is the ongoing consumption of power and chemicals, which is why linked opex unit cost registers are significant.

9.11 Standardisation of reporting of operational events

The cost of delivery of units of work is very valuable information for underpinning budgets, efficiency programmes and plans. But new ways of working, new financial reporting rules and other changing factors make it hard to understand what reported information conveys, as the following case study illustrates.

Case study 13: Rigorous control of costs, accounting treatment and operational practice
An electricity network operator explored how the average repair cost of faults had changed over the previous three-year period. At first, the situation appeared to show an overall modest increase above inflation but there were few obvious trends. This outcome had been expected because of changes to pension costs during this time which had increased the hourly charge of labour to

work. When these new pension costs were removed a high level review indicated there remained some increases but for most fault types, costs had remained stable. This seemed reassuring.

Several months later a more detailed review was held to understand any root causes for fault cost changes over the previous years. At higher voltages – where there may only be a handful of complex urgent and expensive fault repairs – it was hard to spot a trend, but there were some increases at lower voltages. The study identified a number of new factors including the introduction of new jointing kits, new contractor labour rates and other operational issues, such as difficulties in sourcing permissions to dig, opening barriers and deploying traffic lights. These seemed to explain rising trends for 11kv and low voltage fault repair cost increases. However, when the total cost (capex and opex) per regulatory fault was calculated, the whole cost per fault repair was found to have doubled on average over a three-year period. Costs had trebled for some important repair types costs.

It became apparent the true whole cost of a fault repair was altered by capitalisation treatment, which moved the costs from opex to capex. In addition, increases in re-working of faults, which resulted in two and, occasionally, three visits from field staff inflated the cost of fault repair. This factor had not been visible as operational staff viewed several call outs as separate fault repairs, irrespective of the reason for the call out. In a sense this was right – however, it disguised the deeper and costly issue of rising volumes of re-work, some of which was expensive overtime work. This resulted in the company introducing a much more rigorous work management control, dispatch and scheduling system.

Any lack of clarity over the true cost of operational interventions makes the challenge of optimising operational work with the maintenance, repair and capital replacement of assets more difficult. This is a complex subject for all utilities. It is an area of great importance for water and, particularly, waste water utilities due to their complexity, which was explored in Chapter 7. This is one area where the progress being made by the leading utilities is helping to define frontier asset management capability and utility capital efficiency.

Regulatory definitions of events such as faults, gas escapes, process performance and flooding events may also be different from definitions of assets groupings that are used to manage assets.

There are often good reasons why definitions need to be different. For example, any visit to a flooding incident, cable fault or gas escape may require a work order, and operational managers will be keen to manage and control productivity of those visits. However, regulatory definitions are more focused on the impact to the customer and sometimes visits are only recorded depending on the cause of the event. In some cases, regulatory definitions of events, such as flooding, are not sufficiently helpful measures for managing and prioritising work, and other systems must be used.

Regulatory definitions are also changing. This makes alignment of internally (operational) and externally reported (regulated) measures difficult. The solution is to ensure that in the policy plan hierarchy (which was discussed in section 9.2) regulatory objectives are included as Level 1 objectives, and operational objectives are defined at a lower level, with an agreed understanding of how they relate to each other.

9.12   Asset operation and maintenance scheduling

It is essential that day-to-day operational work is driven by and recorded in the same central asset registers and systems that investment and regulatory planning systems use. This is because:

- It is efficient, in that the same use is made of the same asset registers. Indeed any other option results in the duplication of similar data in different asset registers, which is unacceptable.

- It identifies the improvement that arises from the occasional replacement of smaller items of equipment by operations.
- Errors to asset registers are corrected when operational staff discover them.
- Repair and refurbishment events and costs can be collected and allocated to assets. This information, including failure modes and other asset observations, can be used to make capital planning more effective.

Operational scheduling is usually booked to and driven from individual assets, such as particular items of switchgear, probes or pumps. Other work – such as asbestos inspections and site inspection tours – may need to be assigned to sites or facilities. The asset hierarchy allows this to occur but the principle of assigning cost and asset observations to the lowest practical point in the asset hierarchy ensures data is not lost.

Ensuring interventions are planned and recorded and assigned to individuals wherever possible provides useful information for operational control and productivity management tools. These issues are outside the scope of this book, however, the design of all tools needs to reflect the needs of all users of the data. If this is not done, other users will create their own data set and a dangerous and inefficient situation develops in which there are two views of the same situation. With time, these views will diverge and it will become more and more expensive to reconcile them.

9.13 Conclusions

An effective asset management system needs to have all the **tools** that were reviewed in this chapter. Any one of these **tools**, however, could become bureaucratic and soak up valuable time if allowed to do so. The art of establishing an asset management system is to define the degree of **complexity** that is most efficient and effective.

In this chapter we explored the approaches utilities have used to increase the sophistication of 'top-down' planning and 'bottom-up' prioritisation **tools**. With growing sophistication the informal decision making processes need to bridge the gap between these two types of tools changes. In Figure 9.11 we defined four types of decision support processes. Because these informal decision support processes are a consequence of the sophistication of the 'bottom-up' and 'top-down' tools deployed these four types of process also characterise the sophistication of the investment prioritisation and planning elements of the asset management system deployed.

Figure 9.18 illustrates the capability of each of the principle utility sectors to predict future asset performance with the greatest clarity.

Within each sector there are many different utilities operating assets of varying **complexity** in different **climates**. In general, the generation, gas, rail and electricity sectors have the greatest capabilities to predict future asset performance. Although there are a small number of highly critical water treatment processes that are managed with extremely sophisticated asset management tools, the bulk of the water and, particularly, waste water processes and networks are highly **complex** and hard to predict. However, provided

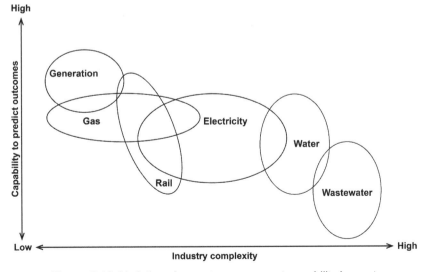

Figure 9.18 Variations in asset management capability by sector

a pragmatic approach is taken, there is substantial value and opportunity in all sectors for further improvements in asset management systems and capabilities.

Notwithstanding the differences between the sectors, the themes that managers feel are important are often the same. Two-thirds of senior utility executives felt the shortage of asset data of some type was a serious issue for their business. For the electricity industries, the data required was better real-time performance and condition data. For the water and waste water sectors, the **complexity** of the asset base means it is a major challenge to understand how such information can be used effectively, something that the industry is tackling.

Collecting asset data is difficult. It takes time and a great deal of thought to obtain it effectively and in a way that avoids duplication (which causes data corruption) but gives all users what they need. The data also needs to be structured so all users can work together to allow cost, risk and performance to be managed. Accordingly, really good data management is a function of a good culture, which requires time, team working, shared objectives, vision and pragmatism. It enables a bright future; but it will not happen by accident and it is easily lost. This clearly creates a number of organisational and team-working issues, which are explored in the following two chapters.

10 Organisation and Organisational Design

10.1 Introduction

In this section we explore how the fifth of the six factors within the asset management capability model, utility **organisation** and organisational design, influences utility asset management capability.

There is no 'best' organisational design for utilities, or any other type of company for that matter. Almost any organisational design can be made to work. In a similar fashion, almost any organisational structure can be made to fail if people are determined it should do so.

The type of **organisation** a utility selects is important because some types create greater distance between information producers and information users. Such **organisations** may create the potential for greater efficiency and effectiveness but, as a consequence, may require more complex transfers of information across the business. If the **tools, teams** and team working needed to do this are not available, the utility will not operate as intended.

10.2 Traditional utility organisational design

As was observed in Chapter 7, for those utilities trading in a benign business climate (illustrated by the 'Calm' or 'Tourist' zones in Figure 7.2) it may be appropriate to control utility performance by controlling the inputs to the utility through, for instance, annual funding and head count controls. Under such circumstances – a production line style of organisation – key tasks and activities are

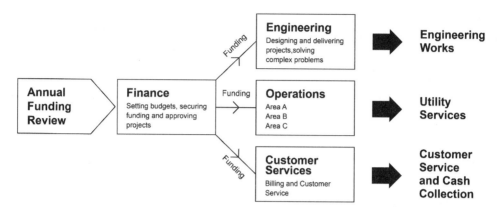

Figure 10.1 Traditional utility organisational design

grouped together. Figure 10.1 illustrates the typical organisational design of such businesses.

Such an organisation can be very effective if there is a ready availability of resources, as in strategy option 2, which was discussed in Chapter 5, section 5.3. However, such organisational designs may not be efficient because local decision makers are unable to identify the most needy projects in the company.

Chapter 6 explored the increasingly challenging climate in which many utilities now operate. This climate places greater constraints on the utility, which can lead to internal tensions. And those tensions are putting more conflict and strain on working relationships at key organisational interfaces as illustrated in Figure 10.2.

Modern utilities operating in more challenging economic climates typified by the 'Stressed' and 'Campaign' zones in Figure 7.2 must manage and reconcile these internal challenges. But this can prove difficult. Case Study 1 in Chapter 7 illustrated a situation in which over-investment occurred in an electricity distribution utility because the construction delivery department had to make complex decisions about replacing components of overhead power lines. If operational departments, already under enormous pressure, are given insufficient support and required to undertake work for which they are ill-equipped, serious inefficiencies can result, as the following case study illustrates.

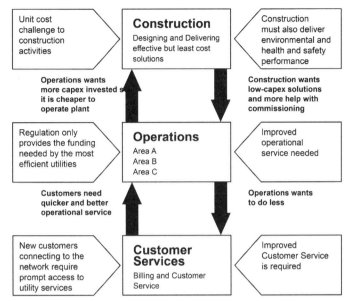

Figure 10.2 Impact of a challenging business climate on the key utility service delivery organisational departments

Case study 1: Scope creep of operational repairs

In response to a sharp decline in waste water treatment compliance performance, which operations felt was partly due to the obsolescence of a range of failing machinery, a company sanctioned operations to create and sponsor an £18m programme of more than 50 refurbishment and improvement projects. The aim of the programme was to quickly fix failing processes with low-risk interventions and repairs. Work was led by local operational and maintenance managers and, after a short review, included the purchase of mobile dewatering equipment, chemical dosing plant, refurbishment of odour control, new instrumentation and control and temporary screening equipment.

The availability of extra staff working on the various refurbishment projects resulted in an almost immediate improvement in operational performance. However, the

complexity of many of the chosen solutions was underestimated and the programme of work was delivered very late, with projects typically costing some 50% more than budgeted. Problems then emerged with temporary power supplies, cleaning of probes and difficulties with delivering and storing chemicals and consumables.

Three years later, staff felt there was little value remaining from the investment. Indeed, at some works there were additional costs to remove abandoned scrap machinery from the site. The project did give a short-term improvement to compliance. In addition to providing extra operational support, the programme made operational staff feel both heard and valued. However, many believed such a situation should never have arisen in the first place and tools that demonstrated operational and asset stress could have helped the situation recover earlier and at less cost.

As pressure builds on a utility, the designers and engineers who direct capital delivery programmes often face great challenges. In the absence of appropriate controls, these designers and engineers may also be forced to take short-term options that destroy long-term value, as the following case study illustrates.

Case study 2: Lack of governance over asset standards
A waste water utility planned the construction of numerous sewage treatment facilities for many rural communities throughout the region. A programme of works and funding had been agreed with the environmental and economic regulators some time earlier. As individual schemes were prepared, however, the utility repeatedly failed to get approval because it was proving to be too expensive. The engineering department was charged with reviewing the asset standards, with a view to generating an affordable solution.

Following a further review, the asset standards were changed to allow the introduction of a number of membrane bio-reactors. Technology providers were confident the technology would be effective while visits to working membrane bio-reactors at other utilities comforted engineering staff. Initially, all seemed well. A number of projects were approved and project managers also found they could deliver projects within budget. However, a combination of poor process performance and a lack of early understanding of the degree of operator training and support necessary resulted in commissioning proving extremely difficult. In the following months high operational costs and erratic compliance resulted in operations staff losing confidence that the equipment could be made to work, and several years later many of the bio-reactors had been replaced at additional cost.

Membrane bio-reactors do work in the right circumstances and with the right level of operator support. But they are low-capex, high-opex solutions and these issues need to be recognised when budgets and commissioning plans are being prepared.

The above case studies illustrate why many modern utilities' organisational design includes a department or team (or several teams) that have the task of managing and co-ordinating the more strategic aspects of the asset management system. Different utilities and utility types hold and name these teams in different ways – such as regulation and asset management, regulation and investment, asset strategy, network management or network strategy. Regardless of the name of the department and the exact scope of its work, its purpose is to co-ordinate and direct the asset management system and so ensure the mix of operating and capital investment work undertaken by the organisation generates the outcomes intended in the company's strategic plan.

These departments also rely on information and advice from key groups in many parts of the utility. Before we proceed further, we need to establish a common understanding of exactly what we mean in an organisational context by the many names we give to the different departments that play key roles in a utility's asset management system.

10.3 The need to define the functional groups that manage a utility's asset management system

It can be difficult to compare the different organisational approaches utilities select because of the significant differences in the meanings of many commonly used organisational terms. For example, many utilities may have an 'asset management' or a 'network strategy' department. They rarely, however, fulfil exactly the same role.

In order to seek clarity and create a common language and understanding, the definition of a number of organisational functional groups in regard to their purpose is generated. In doing so, three issues should be noted:

- Only those functional groups that play key roles in directing and co-ordinating the asset management system will be defined. Accordingly, activities that operate the asset management system and wider utility functions – such as providing customer service – are not addressed.
- Functional groups consist of a group of closely connected tasks that work together to achieve a common purpose. By grouping these tasks together, the need for complex organisational interfaces is reduced.
- Although most choices of functional groups are clear and non-contentious, there are a number of ways and different levels of granularity that could be adopted. However, the objective is to define a language that can be used to discuss utility organisational design.

These functional groups typically vary quite significantly in size and importance from utility to utility. This is largely as a consequence of the varying impact of the six factors in the asset management capability model, which is explored in this chapter. Other company-specific issues, such as previous incidents, legal undertakings and corporate business models, may prove important also.

As most asset management processes and information flows span the organisation, the functional groups have numerous interfaces with each other. Some of these interfaces can be more complex and consideration of these factors is helpful in informing organisational decisions.

In order to create an organisation that can manage its assets, these functional groups may be packaged together into departments or divisions in very different ways. The aim of this chapter is to compare the organisational choices utilities have made while implementing their asset management systems and to establish the underlying principles that are helpful for other utility businesses. For the reasons stated above, while there may be some inadvisable options, there is no 'preferred' or 'best' organisational structure. Indeed, with imagination and tenacity, almost any organisational design can be made to work well – and, likewise, to fail. Furthermore, the process of change itself from one organisational structure to another is a healthy process that can invigorate and refresh a utility.

10.4   A definition of the functional groups that manage the asset management system

The board of directors is ultimately accountable for all the activities in its organisation. Accordingly, responsibility for controlling the asset management system in a utility is delegated from the board through senior management to a number of functional groups. Each of these functional groups has a particular purpose. Although these functional groups can be clearly defined as departments, they are never self-contained because they rely on a community of people across the organisation to support them.

There are a number of ways these functional groups can be defined, and these definitions can adopt different levels of detail and depth. For the purposes of this book, a model has been adopted which considers 12 functional groups as undertaking control of the asset management system. Appendix 3 gives details on the scope of each of these 12 functional groups

Individual functional groups, such as strategic asset data, may actually be overseen by one person in some small utilities. Some functions, such as asset replacement planning, may be handled by several sizable departments in large electricity or rail utilities.

Having now defined the functional groups which run the asset management system, we now consider how utility companies may organise these functional groups into organisational structures.

10.5   Strategic grouping of functional groups

In the previous chapter, we looked at the tools a utility uses to produce effective investment plans and programmes of work, which are needed to undertake the following three tasks:

1. Understand exactly what the utility's stakeholders (corporate and external) want it to achieve. In the first instance, this requires quantifying the top-down pressures and direction.
2. Use bottom-up prioritisation tools that are driven by real-world events and issues – such as the numbers, condition and performance of equipment – to create prioritised lists of interventions. A reconciliation process is then possible to see if and how top-down and bottom up requirements can be accommodated with specific proposals that balance performance, risk and cost. If reconciliation is not possible, it may be necessary to find ways to take risk more sensibly and decrease costs, or explain to stakeholders that the investment objectives are unrealistic.
3. Plan for delivery, prepare detailed programmes of work and execute the agreed investment and operational plans.

A hierarchy that illustrates four levels of strategic content is shown in Figure 10.3.

Organisation and Organisational Design

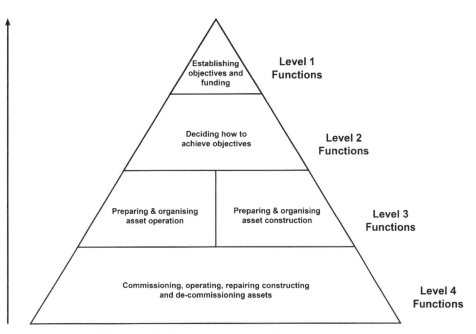

Figure 10.3 Strategy hierarchy of asset managing activities

High performance at every level of this strategy hierarchy is critical if the organisation as a whole is to be efficient and effective. In designing any organisation that is capable of holding constructive tension and delivering high performance at every level, the organisational structure must reflect this strategy hierarchy and prevent strategic decisions whose sole purpose is achieving tactical gains. Not only might this destroy value, but it makes the creation of a performance culture less likely. This is because there is no need for a team operating at one level of the hierarchy to deliver high performance if it is able to 'dip' into the asset management system at a higher level of the hierarchy and change investment, operating or regulatory objectives. These principles apply to all activities at all levels of the strategic hierarchy.

Figure 10.4 categorises each of the 12 functional groups defined earlier into one of three levels in the strategic asset management hierarchy.

Figure 10.4 illustrates the common role that investment

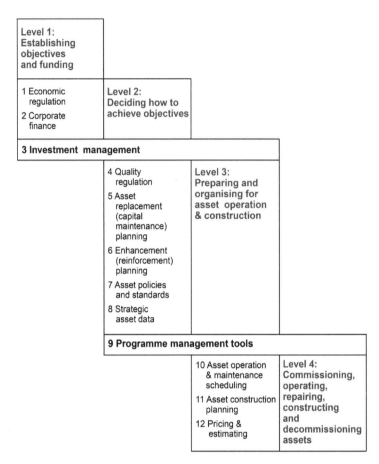

Figure 10.4 Categorisation of asset management functional groups into strategic groupings

management and programme management hold, at different strategic levels, in keeping the formal company record of the company's plans and investment outcomes.

There is value in designing processes and organisational structures to facilitate and control thinking at each level of the strategy hierarchy. At the more strategic levels, a broad understanding of what needs to be achieved and at what cost is necessary before assessing the acceptability of more detailed plans. Similarly, a complete picture of the volume of equipment that needs repair or enhancement is needed before higher-level views on affordability and risk are assessed. A process of iteration can then ensure there is a realistic cascade of plans in place that accommodates real-world issues and risks. This enables delivery of the performance required by stakeholders within agreed funding levels.

In the following three sections the organisational approaches used by different utilities are explored for each of the top three levels of the strategy hierarchy illustrated in Figure 10.3.

10.6   Organisational design of Level 1 functions

In Figure 10.3, we noted the purpose of Level 1 strategic asset managing functions is to establish objectives and funding.

Level 1 functional groups include economic regulation and regulatory corporate finance. Some companies include strategic management of quality regulation at Level 1 if the quality and economic regulators are not cooperating, in which case the utility might be asked to deliver quality initiatives that another regulator is unwilling to fund.

Quality regulation may also play a role in managing Level 1 work when new legislation is under consideration so the cost and benefits of potential new obligations should be considered.

The size and scope of the economic regulation team is proportionate to the degree of challenge that arises from the regulatory climate. Accordingly, Figure 6.1 in Chapter 6 gives a series of tests that provide an insight into the criticality of this function. If a utility is in a challenging regulatory climate, then higher levels of utility complexity, which was reviewed in Chapter 7, will further aggravate the complexity of regulatory management. In contrast, for utilities where the degree of economic regulatory challenge is modest, the economic regulatory function may not occupy a senior position, as the following case study illustrates:

Case study 3: Organisational status of economic regulation in a utility in a benign economic regulatory environment
For some years, this electricity company successfully developed its capability as a modern utility. Its focus was on delivery of infrastructure modernisation programmes and first-time services. In 10 years, it made good progress in this transformation.

More recently, the utility tended to underspend its allowances, which raised tensions. However the utility is still closely aligned with local government and, on the whole, enjoys the co-operation and support of local government. Accordingly, its focus remains on driving the efficient delivery of work and on industrial relations issues. The economic regulation department is staffed by skilled managers and experienced experts with great credibility. The department's manager, however, is several levels of seniority away from a board position. When regulatory issues arise the manager's views are heard, but corporate capability and strategic direction is driven by other, more pressing factors. It is the people who manage those issues who sit on the board.

With growing regulatory maturity and challenge, a number of utilities have experienced the following organisational trends:

- Following privatisation and separation from the state, a small regulatory function would often form within the finance section of the utility, with staff appointed from either engineering or finance. These individuals often were drawn into these roles in the very earliest stages of development of the regulatory activity.
- In the years following privatisation, headcount may often grow until a department of five or six people was reached. At the beginning of this period, with initial regulatory attention focused on financial and budget issues, the location of an economic regulation function within finance is helpful.
- As the economic regulator seeks to define value for money

from investment, the tone of the work undertaken by economic regulation changes and closer working with Level 2 functions is necessary. Finance's support and help in accommodating this change in tone is helpful.

The role of the economic regulation team may also change depending on the stage of the regulatory cycle. In times of price or rate reviews, economic regulation's role in these issues is critical so representation at the most senior level of the company is helpful. In between these reviews, issues such as deliverability of the regulatory contract and reporting issues may mean economic regulation's close working relationship, and possibly co-location, with the Level 2 functions can be very helpful to support this. Different companies, however, may use a variety of approaches successfully. Figure 10.5 illustrates the result of a snapshot review of the organisational seniority of the leaders of the economic regulation team for 38 utility companies.

Figure 10.5 illustrates the following principles, which determine how most utilities organise the most strategic functions within their asset management systems:

1. Utilities that operate in a challenging climate, principally as

Organisational status of the leader of the economic regulation team	Water & wastewater		Gas, electricity & rail		Total
Member of executive team	12		5		17
Reports to member of executive team	With Asset Management	With Finance	With Asset Management	With Finance	
	2	6	4	8	20
Unclear				1	1
Total	20		18		38

Figure 10.5 Organisational seniority of the leaders of economic regulation teams in a sample of 38 different utilities

a consequence of economic regulatory pressure, ensure strong sponsorship of economic regulatory issues on their executive team. This is demonstrated either through attendance by the head of economic regulation or sponsorship of issues by another executive team member with a real interest in the subject, such as the finance director.

2. For the water and waste water sectors, which are more complex to regulate, the inclusion of the head of regulation on the executive team is more common.

3. In the earlier stages of regulatory maturity or in times of challenge, economic regulators look for proof of asset and performance improvement and so extremely close working between Level 1 and Level 2 functional groups is necessary. Some companies have found the collocation or merging of the economic regulation, investment management or other Level 2 functional groups promotes team working and understanding during times of change.

> *Case study 4: Trying to provide regulatory information that does not exist*
>
> *Tom, an investment planning manager for a water utility, was under great pressure. Several years before, a new economic and quality regulatory regime had been introduced and the utility's regulatory department was still seeking to respond to a stream of detailed regulatory queries. It was based in the finance department and had been instructed by its manager to ensure, by year end, that the regulator had approved all outstanding payments in respect of its environmental improvement programme. It was an important issue for the company, particularly as the growing challenge from the regulator could be signalling a change in regulatory tone.*
>
> *"I can't believe it!" said Tom on returning from a meeting with his colleagues in regulation. "They hunt in packs! There were six of them, and that is the third time in three weeks they have*

> *wanted to see me on this issue. Every time I see them, they want more information. They take it away, and come back a week later with more queries and requests. The root of the problem is they have agreed with our regulator that they need to show [..], which is impossible. It doesn't help that the regulator is advised by [name], who worked here for 30 years."*

10.7   The interface between Level 1 and Level 2 functional groups

This interface is extremely important but is not complex because only small groups of people are involved. In the absence of team working, which is discussed in the next chapter, this interface may not function.

Numerous utilities have sought to establish an 'asset owner' organisation, which can hold Level 1 functional groups. This can be made to work well when formal legal contracts are used to subcontract Level 2 or Level 3 work to third parties. However, very careful contract and incentive design are required while contract management and relationship management are both extremely important. These issues are discussed further in the following chapter. When the tone of the relationship has been an 'owner' and a 'tenant' within an organisation, these relationships have proven unstable, as the following case study illustrates.

> *Case study 5: Implementing an asset owner function*
> *A utility seeking to establish an asset owner function wanted to introduce a contractor culture in the organisation. Thirty people reported to the asset owner, which had a clear organisational identity, and whose leader, in turn, reported to the executive director of the regulated division.*
> *The function's challenge was to take control of all regulatory*

licence conditions and major strategic issues. By the end of the first year, however, it became apparent there were fundamental differences between the asset owner and the business delivery organisation. Serious conflict emerged at the interface and the asset owner organisation found it difficult to assert control over a business delivery organisation that employed 99% of staff and set budgets. There always seemed to be a reason why proposals put forward by the owner were not practicable. It did not help that the finance director worked in the business delivery organisation, and the executive director needed to work directly with business delivery, thereby appearing to exclude the asset owner from certain decisions. At one point all staff in the organisation participated in a personal development review – except those in the asset owner's organisation, who were overlooked. Although in itself a minor issue, it sent an unintended message to asset owner staff. The owner/delivery regime was removed shortly afterwards.

Another organisational issue to consider is where to place investment planning in an organisation. There is no right answer to this, as finance, regulation and the Level 2 functional organisation can all hold this function. It is arguably more important finance and regulation have access to investment planning information but investment planning is highly dependent on the provisions of complex information flows from Level 2 functional groups.

Regardless of where it is held, the function needs to ensure key stakeholders are satisfied that the information is impartial and objective by nature. Its purpose is to expose conflicts between the regulatory contract, what spend is intendedand what benefits will accrue. Rigour and change control are, therefore, essential. It is not uncommon for Level 2 functional groups to take a generous view of possible regulatory concessions that may enable additional funding or recognise delivery of outputs. Similarly, finance is more likely to include larger contingencies, plan for the worst and focus on money and expenditure rather than benefits and outputs. If stakeholders do not feel the information prepared by investment management is trustworthy, duplication of investment tracking occurs, which is confusing and expensive.

10.8   Organisational design of Level 2 functions

The purpose of Level 2 strategic asset managing functions in Figure 10.4 was to help decide how objectives could be achieved. Level 2 functional groups include activities such as quality regulation, asset replacement planning, supply and demand planning, asset policies and standards and strategic asset data. At times of price review or rate review, these activities will prepare investment and maintenance proposals, and once the regulatory contract is agreed, they will flex the detail in light of specific events.

Smaller utilities, those supplying 30,000-50,000 households or less, rarely centralise their Level 2 functions. The lack of economies of scale means good tools are generally not available. As a consequence, these utilities are directly managed by staff with personal knowledge of the network and its customer base. These approaches can be very responsive to events and work well with experienced people in post. However, oversight of these teams is difficult and self-interest can take root, while performance and efficiency can tail off. Once this process has started, it is hard to recover lost ground.

The majority of larger utilities elect to centralise much of their Level 2 functional groups into a single department. This process of centralisation often occurs over time if there is a need to achieve greater co-ordination of the asset management system. Typically, the process starts when utilities bring together strategic planning activities from an engineering function and combine them with other strategic operational planning functions. Last to join the department are the functional groups that manage asset replacement planning (maintenance). Premature centralisation of these activities is

(Strategic) Asset Management	32
Network Strategy & Engineering	2
System Management	2
Network Operations	1
Network Management	2
Commercial	1
Investment Planning and Asset Management	2
Total	**42**

Figure 10.6 Organisational names given by 42 different utilities to the departments undertaking their Level 2 asset managing tasks

dangerous without the right team working and tools in place. Some variations exist, with investment planning being included in finance or economic regulation, and for businesses that own several different utilities, each may hold its own Level 2 asset managing department. Most frequently, Level 2 functions are included in the same organisational department and given a variety of departmental names, as the table in Figure 10.6 illustrates.

Figure 10.7 illustrates the organisational seniority of the leaders of the department that holds the majority of each utility's Level 2 functions. In this analysis, where a company holds several different utilities, each organised as a business unit, the leadership team of each of the individual utility business units is considered to be the 'executive team'

A review of the numbers of staff undertaking Level 2 asset managing functions for a range of different utilities does not reveal any obvious trend. This is the case even if account is taken of utility size, complexity and investment levels. This is understandable for four reasons:

Organisational status of leader Level 2 functional organisation	Water & wastewater		Gas, electricity & rail			Total
Member of executive team	16		13			29
Reports to member of executive team	With construction	With operations	With operations	With finance	With commercial	
	2	2	3	1	1	9
Total	20		18			38

Figure 10.7 Organisational seniority of the leader of the Level 2 asset management department

1. **The exact scope of the work undertaken by the Level 2 asset managing functions changes.** For most utilities, the Level 2 functions undertake a similar purpose, although different utilities undertake the work to different levels of detail. For example, some utility's Level 2 functions define the scope of work required; others include a great deal of detail. These issues are important for defining the organisational interface between Level 2 and Level 3 functional groups. This is one of the most significant features of utility organisational and process design, and this point is explored in section 10.9 below.

2. **The prime goal of the functional groups that control the asset management system is to ensure they produce effective proposals.** This is not to say that efficiency is not important – it is. Furthermore, a culture that is not seen to embrace efficiency in all parts of a business sends out the wrong message to the operational departments that have the challenge of driving ever-greater efficiency. However, the marginal cost of producing effective plans on time is insignificant compared with the risk of preparing poor plans or delivering them late, as case study 2 in Chapter 8 illustrated.

3. **Staff numbers are dependent on the effectiveness of the asset**

management tools used by the utility. In Section 9.7.3 in Chapter 9, we explored the four types of decision-support processes that operate in the decision-making gap and which fall between top-down planning and bottom-up prioritisation systems. The Type 1 tools (budget-constrained local decision making) effectively delegates authority within certain boundaries to operational staff. Accordingly, lower levels of central resources are required in the Level 2 planning functions. Conversely, Type 2 processes (centralised review) may be more effective but require much higher levels of resources to review proposals. However, as Type 3 and, particularly, Type 4 tools and decision-support processes are implemented, staff numbers typically fall and effectiveness rises.

4. **Required capability of the asset management system.** Depending on the climate and internal complexity of a utility (two factors from the asset management capability model which were discussed in Chapters 6 and 7) there may be a need for a more or less capable asset management system. A less complex asset management system, which may be ideal for a company in the 'Tourist' segment of Figure 7.2, is simpler to operate and will require less complex tools and fewer staff.

There is some evidence of a broad correlation between utility investment levels and numbers of staff undertaking Level 2 functions, if account is taken of the predominant types of investment undertaken by the utility. The figure below compares annual capital investment with the numbers of staff working on Level 2 asset management tasks for 19 different utilities.

The broad correlation observed above may be driven by the nature of enhancement projects, which tend to be larger projects with a clear purpose and need. For these types of projects, there are fewer planning options but more of the risks lie in detailed design, construction and solution delivery. Conversely, utilities managing a

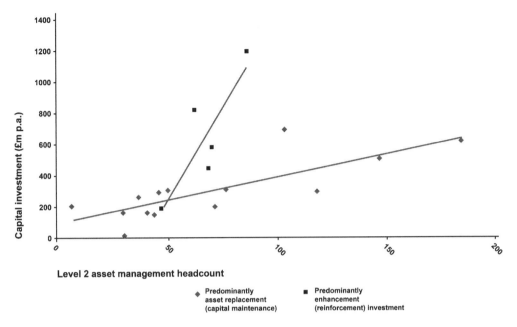

Figure 10.8 Capital investment versus Level 2 asset management headcount

higher proportion of asset replacement work typically select initiatives from hundreds of smaller types of interventions. The object of this investment is to control the cumulative cost, performance and risk of complex utility plant and networks. This type of work is more complex to plan.

10.9 The interface between Level 2 and Level 3 functional groups

As was seen earlier in Figure 10.3, the role of Level 2 functional groups is to decide how the organisation can achieve its objectives. In practice, this means drawing up programmes of work and matching budgets. This work is then passed on to Level 3 functions for delivery during the investment approval process.

However, there is a great temptation for staff working on Level 2 planning to continue working on marginally better options, as case study 12 in Chapter 9 illustrated. As a consequence, in most utilities the staff who have the challenge of delivering work programmes frequently ask for earlier approval of work and greater visibility of future work. This can be achieved through a combination of three approaches that smooth the approval and handover processes, driving the flow of work from planning (Level 2) to organising and scheduling (Level 3). These three approaches are:

1. **Clarity of the approval processes**: Figure 9.17 in Chapter 9 detailed typical project and programme maturity milestones. This type of methodology ensures the criteria at each stage of approval are clear. Not only does this ensure sufficient detail is presented at each stage of approval, but it also empowers staff to resist premature challenges from senior managers on points of detail that might delay approval. It is not unusual for senior staff to think of new options at late stages of the approval process that they feel should have been considered. If this happens often, senior staff should be encouraged to get involved earlier to ensure their advice is secured at the right point in the approval process. Staff who produce the plans can then be given objectives to secure approval for specific volumes of work without prejudicing quality and value. Senior staff can also ensure projects are not 'overworked' by Level 2 planning staff, as this reflects a loss of time which could have been used to design and deliver projects more efficiently.

2. **Clarifying the work handover process**: At some point in the approval process work must move from Level 2 planning and shaping to Level 3 designing and delivering. The 'scope and solution 'approval stage detailed in Figure 9.17 is a logical handover, and it marks the point at which the cost, risk and benefit of the proposal are reasonably clear. However, Level 2 functional staff do not have the resources of skills to optioneer engineering work. Accordingly, the early appointment at the needs or initiation stage of a project or

programme manager who organises and supervises this work is helpful. This also gives Level 3 delivery and design staff early visibility of work, and ensures they can take ownership for all decisions made prior to their formal ownership of the project.

3. **Move from projects to programmes**: Approval of individual projects is sometimes necessary but with imagination, programme approval is possible. Top-down planning can identify the criteria that characterise the neediest projects. Approval of these criteria and a matching level of funding allow a programme manager to focus on identifying and delivering the most needy projects from a larger pool of prospective work. By approving programme criteria and funding levels that represent 50%-80% of expected affordable work volumes, the risk of approving what later transpires to be too much investment can be managed. This process can work well for switch-gear replacements, water and gas main replacement work, overhead line refurbishment programmes and substation civil structures maintenance. These techniques can involve a considerable degree of delegation, and become more applicable (without abdication) for utilities that have sufficient information to make most use of the Type 3 and 4 decision-support processes that were discussed in Section 9.7.3.

10.10 Functional and geographical organisational strategies

Traditionally, utilities employed geographical organisational designs. Thirty years ago, there was no need for Level 2 functional groups in utilities, with the possible exception of enhancement planning function, which engineered major new projects. In this model regionally based operational and construction staff had the accountability to run, operate and maintain geographical sections of the utility network efficiently and safely. These staff also held most of the knowledge and experience of the network and planning work, and quality regulation was undertaken under the direction of regional managers. This traditional model ensured clear accountability for service delivery. These organisational arrangements were excellent at responding to events. However with such traditional organisational models it can be difficult for managers and regulators to decide if such businesses are efficient and conflict between regions and programmes of work can be more difficult to resolve.

The development of the tools discussed in Chapter 9 enables utilities to create corporate asset information that can be made available to all staff. Asset replacement planning staff can be more effective and proactive if they manage groups of assets rather than regional budgets. Historically, a district manager may have requested help from the engineering department because equipment failures were causing compliance problems and extra overtime costs. An engineer would probably have visited the district manager, listened to the problems and, with their staff, drawn up proposals with a view to addressing the issues. In a modern utility, however, the availability of company-wide breakdown and maintenance reports, accurate asset register and equipment productivity information enables an asset replacement planning analyst to take a more objective look at the issue. It might be that this review shows similar equipment is successfully operated elsewhere, and more careful operation or maintenance may be all that is needed.

Other activities, such as programme management, would have traditionally been undertaken on a district basis, but better information these days allows that to happen centrally. Figure 10.9 illustrates the sorts of trends that have occurred in many utilities over the last 15 years.

The introduction of more centralised Level 1 and 2 functions has increased capability, reduced planning costs and centralised control. But the process of centralising control also threatens to undermine

Functional group	Traditional	Modern
1 Economic Regulation	Not needed	Centralised
2 Corporate Finance	Centralised: Only required to aggregate regional programme management spend as part of budgeting.	Centralised
3 Investment Management	Not needed	Centralised
4 Quality Regulation	Regional supporting (Level 3) role	Centralised (Level 2 or 1 role)
5 Asset Replacement (Capital Maintenance) Planning	Decisions made regionally by operational managers (reactive)	Centralised & Functional (pro-active) Regional (reactive)
6 Enhancement (Reinforcement) Planning	Centralised (as an engineering department)	Centralised
7 Asset Policies and Standards	Centralised (as an engineering department)	Centralised & Functional
8 Strategic Asset Data	Not needed	Centralised
9 Programme Management	Regional	Centralised

Figure 10.9 The impact of modern asset management systems on the organisational design of level 1 and level 2 functional groups

the personal accountability that operational staff have traditionally held for delivering operational service. If operational staff lose faith in the degree of support they can expect to receive from the Level 2 planning and organisational functions, performance and compliance failure is likely. In such circumstances, the utility can become inefficient and ineffective, which is a disastrous outcome. The fundamental issues of teams and team working that stem from this are explored in the next chapter.

10.11 The degree and pace of change

In addition to the appetite for team working, the degree and pace of transformation and centralisation that is possible depends on the effectiveness of the tools. Less complex utilities find it easier to develop more effective tools. For these reasons, the electricity, gas, rail and highways sectors have been particularly successful in implementing these approaches.

For more complex and unpredictable utilities – which Chapter 7 identified as notably the water and waste water utilities – implementation of these new ways of working is much more difficult. As was noted earlier, premature implementation of centralised functional planning and prioritisation approaches can be disastrous.

Introducing centralised proactive planning processes and organisational structures into utility sites, which are closely supervised or manned, risks even greater challenges. Because site staff can see with their own eyes the condition and performance of their assets, they see less value in updating asset registers. Furthermore, site staff often hold strong views rich in detail on what work needs to be done at their site.

A controlled and gradual process of change and centralisation is underway currently in most utilities. To put this issue in perspective, it is a process of thoughtful evolution, as opposed to revolution. As the case study below illustrates, there may be many asset types and operational processes that will and should still be managed locally by their operators 20 years from now.

Case study 6: The migration from geographical to centralised management of waste water treatment plant
A division of a large waste water treatment utility wanted to explore where data and knowledge existed in its business and how to move it from a local (expert judgement) to a centralised (functional) managed maintenance.

The long service of many of its operational, maintenance and construction staff meant, amongst them, they had an extraordinary total of 18,600 man years of service. Estimating the equivalent information contained in the GIS and equipment registers was difficult. At most, there were 2,800 man years of data input in both these systems, the accumulation of the previous 60 years. As this data was static and much of it involved enhancing the quality of the data on the same assets the value of the comparison was questionable. By any measure, however, the value of the data in the corporate registers was a fraction of that held by staff.

A review of condition assessments revealed insufficient rigour in condition grade assessments and meant time-based trends of equipment condition were difficult to interpret for equipment assets, although small but valuable quantities of performance information was available for the more critical assets. Quite excitingly, streams of good cheap asset performance data became available as a consequence of a decision made years before to specify a common digital equipment 'web enabled' protocol.

However, data collection metrics indicated that the top-down planning capability needed 10 to150 times less data than the bottom-up prioritisation methodology. This is because 'top down' could use samples of data for whole groups of assets to get useful information, whereas the bottom-up methodology needed a number of asset-specific observations for each asset. Both methodologies required similar information on failure modes, consequences of failure and unit costs, since much of this was asset-group specific and not usually asset specific. The review concluded:

- *Most of the businesses' real knowledge was in the heads of its staff.*
- *The top-down planning regime required large volumes of data but still needed far less data than bottom-up processes.*

> • *However, with care, 'top down' and 'bottom up' could and should share the same architecture.*
> • *By successively targeting the application of bottom-up techniques to higher performance, risk and cost assets, significant benefits could be realised without unnecessary cost and complexity.*

10.12 Organisational clarity

Achieving organisational and process clarity are key objectives in any organisational design. These are specialist subjects for which there is a considerable body of support and literature available[1].

Once an organisation has defined its key functional groups, construction of processes to enable these functional groups to work together is possible. Prior to doing so, agreeing principles is helpful. It is useful to agree which functional groups take a lead on managing and sponsoring programme and project work through the investment approval processes. Given that the cost and benefit of work is unclear until scope and solution approval (see Figure 9.17), there is value in Level 2 functional groups sponsoring work until that point, although it is essential Level 3 functional groups are fully involved long before any handover. This can place a considerable burden on Level 2 functional groups, which illustrates the benefit of developing policies and standards so that programmes of work can be approved at the scope and solution stage. Once any principles are agreed, tools such as the RACI matrix (see Figure 10.10) are helpful for teasing out interfaces.

By pinning down accountabilities and responsibilities to work group leaders, high-level clarity can be generated, and more detail can then be sought.

[1] An excellent book on this subject titled 'Organizational Design: A step-by-step Approach', is written by Richard Burton, Gerardine DeSanctis and Borge Obel and published by Cambridge University Press, ISBN 978-0-521-61733-8

A	**Accountable:** This role cannot be delegated, the buck stops here
R	**Responsible:** Responsibility can be delegated by the Accountable person to the responsible person
C	**Consult:** This person should be consulted when decisions are made
I	**Inform:** This person should be informed

Figure 10.10 RACI matrix for use in designing lean processes

10.13 Conclusions

Traditionally, utility efficiency was driven by a controlling finance department that restricted the availability of resources. Until recently, the delivery of services was managed by locally based frontline management, which ensured productivity and efficiency was prioritised. These frontline teams held all the knowledge of how to operate and maintain the network in their particular neighbourhoods – the scope and quality of work was their choice. They were supported by engineering, maintenance and other support services. In times of crisis, which for an under-funded utility can be quite often, these teams are outstanding at resolving difficult situations. Their commitment and accountability has been exceptional.

With the advent of greater pressures on utilities to demonstrate effectiveness, greater levels of internal conflict have been created. The centralisation of support services means frontline staff have less control over service provision. In addition, rather than doing what they can with available funding, frontline staff are required to achieve certain service outcomes, at a time when their budgets are being reduced.

In order to better manage internal conflicts, these new pressures suggest greater control over asset management systems is necessary. In part, this may be achieved by better use of tools, which allow performance, risk and value to be much more clearly seen and managed. These issues were discussed in the previous chapter. In order to accommodate new ways of working, organisational designs are being shaped by two pressures:

1. **The need for greater strategic direction:** In order to ensure the type of services provided are shaped by strategic issues – such as the affordable level of risk and quality – customers are prepared to pay for new processes and activities introduced by utilities. This involves the evolution of several layers of processes and organisational design, which manage work and value at different levels of strategic need. At the highest level (Level 1), small numbers of finance and regulatory staff lead the definition of the regulatory contract. At a lower level (Level 2), staff decide how the regulatory contract should be delivered. These groups or teams are given names such as 'asset management' or 'network strategy'. At the next level (Level 3), teams explore how work actually needs to be delivered, given practical constraints. At Level 4, many thousands of people may be involved in the huge challenge of building, operating, repairing and maintaining the utility network. A higher level is not more important than a lower level. All levels are essential and need to work together, treating each other with respect, delivering excellent service to each other and ensuring proposals are acceptable, practical and deliverable.

2. **The need for efficiency and less reactive ways of working:** In order to become more efficient and more proactive, a trend is underway of increasingly central control over performance, risk and cost. This results in the emergence of specialist strategic functions that are capable of pro-actively managing asset types from across the whole organisation.

Although a number of trends and themes are evident, there is no 'best' organisational design for utilities. Almost any organisational design can be made to work with an asset management system that is driven by the right mix of tools and teams. In a similar fashion, almost any organisational structure can be made to fail if people are determined it should do so. Lastly, the process of change itself is helpful for stimulating innovation, change and renewal.

As a consequence of these trends, utility organisational structures are becoming much more complex than has been the case historically. For example, in a modern utility organisation there may be a centralised asset management function, which itself may contain functional and geographically orientated teams. In construction departments, work may be organised and focused on particular contractors while in operations, staff will invariably be based locally and manage geographical segments of very different types of equipment and processes. Excellent tools and really clear organisational clarity are needed to ensure all these approaches work together.

However, a challenge remains. The growth of centralisation and functionalisation threatens to undermine the traditional local accountability frontline staff have held. In addition, frontline staff are continually asked to achieve ever-increasing performance outcomes while their freedom to act is constrained by the availability of resources and the performance of their equipment. In practice, it is hard to tell if frontline staff perform poorly or have, in fact, been put in an impossible position by the organisation. Without good teams and excellent team working, these issues cannot be tackled.

11 Teams and Team Working

11.0   Introduction

In this chapter we look at the last of the six factors in the asset management capability model: **teams**, team working and the management of relationships.

In the previous chapter, we saw how the development of new **tools** and the adoption of new **organisations** can give utilities greater control over their asset management systems and allow more effective and efficient ways of working. That said, positive behaviours and excellent team working can also enable poor **tools** or complex **organisations** to work, and even work well. In contrast, the absence of team working may mean the simplest organisations and best **tools** will fail to deliver performance.

Teams and team working operate on a number of different levels, from small sports clubs to political and ideological groups of many thousands. Research, however, indicates people find social groupings and tribes of more than 150 difficult to maintain[1]. Studies of internet gaming reveal cohesive groups of up to 60 individuals can be comfortably maintained in the same system of rules. For more complex relationships (such as creative networks where intense team working is needed), however, groups greater than 12 can become unstable[2]. For a utility to be successful, good team working at all these levels is essential for the individual and for the company.

1 Dunbar, R.I.M. (1992) *Neocortex size as a constraint on group size in primates,* Journal of Human Evolution 22: 469-493.
2 Mayfield, Ross. "An Ecosystem of Networks". February 18, 2003, from http://radio.weblogs.com/0114726/2003/02/12.html

The most important team is the executive team, or the board, while numerous other social and tribal groups will also operate in a utility. The importance of creating strong **teams** and cooperative behaviours is recognised and covered in many other studies and management books. Accordingly, only specific 'team working' and 'relationship' issues that relate to utilities are addressed in this chapter.

11.1 The asset management capability model

Good team working is something most staff want. It is also essential for corporate performance. An effective organisation with great team working is able to efficiently call on resources from across the organisation to work on important tasks. However, it is hard to achieve, and even more so when working relationships are challenged by competing local objectives. Good team working is easier to achieve for an uncomplicated utility operating in a benign climate where the corporate goals only call for either high efficiency or high effectiveness. But in a challenging climate, a complex utility that is driven by a simultaneous need for high efficiency and effectiveness faces an enormous internal challenge. If the organisation's tools are poor, staff are left to quantify and articulate risk, performance and the cost of different competing options. In such situations the good faith of teams is more likely to be tested beyond breaking point, with a much greater risk of process fracture and dispute.

Most utilities that target high performance will have experienced such circumstances several times in at least some part of their business. As a consequence, it may be more realistic to consider two things: that the failure of team working and subsequent dispute is a natural stage for any utility striving for high performance, and that chaos is only avoided each day by strong teams that make their tools and organisations work.

11.2 Constructive tensions

Modern utilities are complex organisations. As part of the qualitative attitudinal survey, the results of which were summarised earlier in Figure 9.5, utility staff were asked what others could do to make their own jobs easier. This revealed several areas of constructive tension that were common to all utilities that target high performance. These areas of constructive tension are usually driven by departmental dependencies. These major points of tension from other departments are as follows:

- **Economic and quality regulation and corporate finance (Level 1 functional groups):** Concern from the rest of the company that the Level 1 functional groups will agree, to or set, regulatory targets or budgets that are undeliverable.
- **Asset management/network strategy (Level 2 functional groups detailed in Figure 10.5, except quality regulation):** Anxiousness from construction staff that the Level 2 functional groups will spend too long planning and thinking, and not give construction staff the time they need to deliver projects. Concern from operational staff that Level 2 functional groups will agree new policy and principles that are unaffordable and that capital investment will not be allocated to the right projects in time to allow operational compliance and minimise operating costs.
- **Operational planning and operations:** Anxiousness amongst asset management and construction teams that operational staff have an endless appetite for capital investment, some of it caused by harsh operating and descoped maintenance and lubrication regimes. Asset management staff are particularly concerned that capital investment will become exhausted on inappropriate projects championed by operations, which results in a need to overspend capital allowances in order to address high profile issues. Construction staff are concerned

they will be forced to overspend project approvals in order
to fund last minute requirements from operations during the
commissioning of new plant.

- **Construction:** Concern in asset management and operational
  departments that construction staff will de-scope or defer
  the difficult or expensive parts of projects to prevent projects
  from overspending. There is also often concern construction
  will not deliver, or that they will blame cost overruns on poor
  planning by asset management and economic regulation.

However, each of the organisational groupings detailed above
also has its own concerns. For example:

- **Economic/quality regulation and finance**: these departments
  are anxious to ensure cost shocks do not occur, and
  erroneous regulatory reports, based on flawed source data
  provided by colleagues, are avoided.
- **Asset management/network strategy**: these departments
  continually looks for the information needed to manage asset
  risk and performance. They require confirmation that agreed
  plans and proposals will be delivered to time and budget by
  operations and construction. They seek to ensure operating
  and maintenance practice and operating cost pressures do not
  create a need for non-essential additional capital investment.
- **Operational planning and operations:** these departments
  strive to achieve operational performance outcomes dictated
  by others, with availability of resources also controlled by
  others. Operational staff often have strongly held local views
  on where investment should be targeted. Well meant though
  these views are they are frequently inconsistent with
  corporate priorities.
- **Construction:** construction teams are concerned that work
  and funding will be released to it too late to allow delivery. In
  addition, the availability of operational resources to allow
  design, delivery and commissioning is frequently a concern.

Utility executives and managers are similar to any other business leader. They are often proud of what has been achieved, but remain unsatisfied with the performance. They see scope for improvement, and invariably have plans underway to make such changes. However, reflecting back on the team working challenges addressed in recent years, all leaders recollected major periods of internal challenge and conflict. The following case studies illustrate the types of events most utilities have experienced in their business at some time or another. These reflections from 13 senior executives also illustrate the passion and energy business leaders need when constructive tension threatens to boil over:

Case study 1: Recollections and observations on utility organisational and structural change from 13 utility executives:

1. *"A key challenge is to overcome tribalism, with individual teams only focused on trying to do their job. At best, it leads to everyone thinking they have done a great job but the poor outcome is someone else's fault."*

2. *"When we first introduced the concept of asset management, many people felt the asset management teams were intruding. For us, it quickly led to strife. In fact, it got so bad in the end we had to get in an independent facilitator."*

3. *"At one point, asset management seemed to think operations did not need brains."*

4. *"For a while, we had 'capital maintenance', 'restoration' and 'inspections' functions. It was great for focus but the behaviours were poor. For example, the restoration teams seemed to expect first call on all the resources they asked for, and so in each district operational people stopped sharing resources and started pretending no one was available."*

5. *"Until quite recently, each of the regions decided what work it needed to do. However, there was no standardisation and people did what they could, rather than what they should. When we tried to force standardisation some solutions were*

ridiculous. It was as if some people went out of their way to show what we were trying to do was impractical by not using any common sense."

6. *"Some people in asset management started talking about asset ownership. When I heard that I stopped it. It's not helpful – it introduces a culture of hierarchy, which is divisive."*

7. *"We never really seemed to be one team. But we had lots of teams, and some of them were really good teams. Many of them had their own tee shirts."*

8. *"For a period the construction teams had a tough time. They were under pressure to deliver the investment programme but operational managers were under such pressure they could not help with design. When it came to commissioning there were arguments. The often high running costs and maintainability of equipment became big issues."*

9. *"At some point, we seemed to lose our asset management department. It started with making them more responsive to operations, which was a good thing. However, budgets got carved up and broken into regional allowances and key staff were seconded to regions. The planning staff became more and more involved in operational work to the extent they didn't seem to do any planning. A year later, we were almost completely reactive, and important regulatory targets were not being achieved."*

10. *"To get clarity, we went through a complex process-mapping exercise. However, we never seemed to be able to do it in enough detail. For example, people used the high-level processes to justify why they didn't need to provide information to us."*

11. *"Most people wanted clarity, but not everyone. Clarity also took away some of the engineers' freedom. For some of the really experienced engineers, we found that if they disagreed with a particular engineering solution, they fought it tooth and nail."*

> 12. *"As we starting introducing the asset management way of working, the [region] was a closed shop to us. It even had its own files and records and surprised us at year-end by telling us what it had done and what it cost."*
>
> 13. *"Operational staff seemed to think the only purpose of a project in their area was to allow them to book time to it in between real work. All the work near to [the depot] was done quite quickly. However, some projects were four years old and couldn't be closed as some difficult bits, like road or river crossings, remained. There was always a reason, like they couldn't get access to land. However, it meant our unit costs were out of date, and a rump of over-spending projects was not identified and projects had four years of unfunded and unapproved inflation to pay."*

Very few utility staff make their colleagues' work more difficult out of malice. Indeed, a common feature of utility staff across the world is they take great pride in their work and hold a very clear belief that their work is worthwhile and important. However, this self-belief and passion mean utility staff will resist doing something that, in their frame of reference and experience, is wrong. Accordingly, the greatest challenge for utility leaders is to understand and address misunderstanding and explain why new ways of working are necessary.

11.3   Quantifying utility attitudes and misconceptions

During preparation of this book a quantative attitudinal survey was undertaken to explore the differences in attitude between utility staff working in different parts of utilities.

11.3.1 Survey methodology

The survey was targeted at staff working and leading the asset management, construction and operational departments of 14 utilities. These organisational groupings map on to the Level 2 and Level 3 functions detailed earlier in Figure 10.4.

Initial questions categorised which department the respondent worked in and which departments they believed they could be working in three years' time. Each person was then asked to rank their views of the quality of services they gave and received from each of the other two departments. People were asked to select a first and second best answer from a range of structured answers. The answers to all questions followed the same structure detailed in Figure 11.1, which also details the inferred meaning of the various answers people gave.

Nature of departmental relationship \\ Is a positive outcome expected?	Yes and People want to help me	Quite likely and People will help if I do more	Unlikely/ not really and People need to do more and so help me	No and People don't/ won't help me	War and No one wants to help anyone
Very well/good	**Answer (a)** Success very likely, as usual				
Quite good	**Answer (b)** Success likely, we find a way through problems	**Answer (c)** Successes likely but there are issues and I have ideas			
Quite poor			**Answer (d)** Success unlikely but they are under pressure	**Answer (e)** Success unlikely; they don't believe our need/values	
Very poor				**Answer (f)** They have other priorities/feel threatened	
War					**Answer (g)** No one wants to help me, and it's mutual
Interpretation	Our and their values and reasoning are aligned	Our reasoning is not aligned with theirs	Their reasoning is not aligned with ours	Their values are not aligned with ours	No one has any interest in aligning our respective values

Figure: 11.1 Structured team working survey methodology

11.3.2 Undertaking the survey

A total of 52 staff working in different departments of 14 different utilities were asked their view of how well they were providing, and getting, good service from their colleagues. By design, the results are not statistically significant for any one utility. However, a number of industry-wide trends emerged by combining the results. The results of the survey are summarised in Figure 11.2.

11.3.3 Survey conclusions

Asset management staff consider themselves more likely to be working in operations or construction within three years. In contrast, operational staff and construction staff felt it unlikely they will move departments in the medium term. This may reflect the reality that

Question asked / Nature of answer given	Yes — and People want to help me	Quite likely — and People will help if I do more	Unlikely/ not really — and People need to do more and so help me	No — and People don't/ won't help me	War — and No one wants to help anyone
Do you get good support from asset management staff?	Asset Management		Operations Construction		
Do you get good support from operations staff?	Operations	Asset Management Construction			
Do you get good support from construction staff?		Asset Management Operations Construction			
Do asset managers have the data they need?		Construction	Asset Management Construction		
Do asset managers change policy and provide urgent funding quickly?			Asset Management Operations Construction		
Does asset management give construction staff early visibility of work programmes?		Asset Management	Construction		

Figure 11.2 Results of the team working survey

asset management is a small department and career development can be restricted if staff are not organisationally mobile. However the fact that 90% of career options are outside asset management may also be helpful in moderating the behaviour of asset management staff. As one asset manager summarised:

> "*You have to be careful who you annoy. You never know where you will be working next year.*"

Additional key points to note are:

1. **Asset management service**: Asset managers felt they received very good support from their colleagues in their own department. Construction and operational staff, on the other hand, felt they received quite a poor service from asset management. Furthermore, operational and construction staff believed that asset managers needed to do more to improve the service they provided.
2. **Operational service:** Operations staff also felt they had very good support from colleagues in their own department. Asset managers and construction staff felt they got help most of the time from operational staff.
3. **Construction service:** Construction staff felt they gave quite good support to their own colleagues. Operational and asset management staff felt they also received quite a good service, and all recognised they could do more to make the relationship work even better.
4. **Asset information:** Construction staff felt asset managers' need for asset information was "pretty well" satisfied. However, asset managers and operational staff agreed that asset managers' data requirements were "not that well" satisfied. However both operations and asset management felt others needed to do more to resolve this issue. Closer analysis of the survey results indicated that the problems for the water and waste water sectors seemed much more acute

than for the electricity sectors. There was also evidence that senior staff in asset management were more concerned about information gaps than less senior staff.

5. **Quick policy changes and funding provision:** All three departments seemed to agree that asset managers were not able to amend policy and provide needed funding quickly. On average, staff from all departments felt others needed to do more to resolve these issues. Scores from operations and construction were reasonably consistent on this issue. However, although asset managers' scores averaged out to suggest they were unsatisfied at their ability to change policy and provide funding quickly, individual scores were extremely wide ranging.

6. **Visibility of future work programmes:** Asset managers felt they were giving construction staff good visibility of future programmes of work but construction staff consistently disagreed.

On a number of the more contentious issues, such as the availability of asset data and asset managers' success at amending policy and providing funding, wide ranges of scores lay beneath the headline average figures. Extremely different scores to similar questions in some companies indicated strongly divergent views within that organisation.

11.4   Utility team working strategies and approaches

This is a complex and important subject that is better covered in more general work. Only those aspects of this issue that relate to the asset management system of a utility organisation are addressed.

Promoting good team working and a high performance culture in complex utilities is easier if there is greater clarity about issues that could prove to be contentious or divisive. It is much easier for teams to discuss facts and change approaches than it is to ask others to compromise their own performance objectives on the basis of one person's opinion. Various utility leaders have used a number of different approaches to achieve this.

Clearly, the development of a range of tools and information approaches, which articulate asset risk and value, are great vehicles for allowing different teams to work together to choose the best options for the organisation's stakeholders. This was discussed earlier in Chapter 9. A similar and complementary approach is to ensure themes, such as a practical and robust health and safety approach, unite values and underpin every decision. The concept that any accident is avoidable and over-investment in one area may create risks and dangers for staff elsewhere is a powerful technique for aligning values and interests.

This approach was successfully used by DuPont, the chemical company, on its gunpowder manufacturing plants. Traditional design for these explosive factories used numerous buildings isolated from the rest of the site. These buildings had three thick masonry walls, and a roof and a fourth wall made of thin timber. When there was an explosion the roof and the wooden wall would allow the blast to be dissipated over vacant land and the three sturdy walls would protect the rest of the site from damage. Enormous resentment was caused when the family of dead workers had to scour the country side seeking to recover as many parts of their loved ones as they could for burial. This approach, which sought to manage the consequences of explosions rather than its root causes, proved highly divisive. However by requiring plant managers and their families to live on the operational site, DuPont ensured a company-wide common sense of ownership of health and safety issues was ingrained into decision-making.

Many utility leaders also have observed events or issues that either catalysed or heralded new ways of working. Case study 1 in chapter 9 illustrated how a process of change was initiated by a new and urgent need for an electricity company to respond to the consequences of storms. However, there are also examples of leadership inspiring change before crisis sets in. For example, in multi-utility organisations, composed of water and electricity or water and waste water utilities, the efficient and effective division of resources between the utility businesses requires vision and team working, as the following case study illustrates:

> *Case study 2: For the greater good*
>
> *For some years, a water and waste water utility had enjoyed improving performance in its water division. It had been tough, but leakage levels were broadly under control and a strong team had successfully responded, over a number of years, to the new challenges imposed by modern drinking water standards. The investment and network strategy team, in particular, was extremely effective and planning and rate review documents typically were well prepared, and the funding had followed.*
>
> *In contrast, the waste water planning team was under immense pressure. Eight out of 11 of the major issues facing the utility company as a whole were waste water issues. The data and tools available to run the waste water utility were of a much poorer quality and waste water requests for funding were invariably a string of reactive and locally championed requests for funding for particular issues. The company went through a process of introducing fortnightly and monthly structured risk-based decision-making reviews to support, challenge and prioritise all investment requests. Resources and management attention moved from water to waste water to support this approach, which proved to be highly contentious. However, by comparing the risk profiles of the water and waste water utilities, the need for this change was demonstrated to operational and asset management staff.*

In other utilities, leaders have reminded their colleagues they face an external challenge or opportunity. For example, an incoming executive at a demoralised and poorly performing utility business reminded his new colleagues that, several years before, they had worked for one of the most effective utilities in the sector. He observed the utility was still serving the same customers, facing the same challenges and employing the same people, more or less. In this way, he gave them hope that they could soon be working in a highly performing business if they wanted to do so. This gave everyone a realistic, credible common external objective to strive towards and engendered a team working ethic across the organisation. Several years later, the utility was delivering upper-quartile performance once again.

A different approach which a number of utilities have used very successfully to address extremely complex issues has been to reorganise in such a fashion that new teams are created with a narrower but very clear purpose and mandate. The creation of new divisions or the formation of alliances or outsourcing arrangements with third parties can give parts of the asset management system great clarity and imperative. New commercial interfaces mean the relationships between teams and divisions which can be fudged or neglected in a large organisation must receive the attention and focus they deserve, as the following case study illustrates:

Case study 3: The importance of organisational interfaces in resolving internal conflicts of interest

An important objective for the electricity industry is to secure strong commercial control over network refurbishment investment projects. This is not as easy as it sounds. When overhead lines are being refurbished, work may occur at different points over quite extensive routes. The practicalities of securing land access, taking the line off supply and the impact of weather may mean individual projects can take several years to complete.

During that time, it would not be unusual for a project to have several different project managers. In addition, the project management role itself is particularly challenging for two reasons. Firstly, project managers need to use specialist equipment and employ craftsman, such as linesmen and jointers, whose primary role is to respond to operational events and who generally report to operational managers. Getting access to these resources at the moment the project needs them can be difficult. Secondly, issues – such as the discovery of boggy ground or 'pole top rot' or a farmer's new requirement for a pole to be moved – become apparent during construction, which call for unplanned work.

An increasing number of a particular utility's network projects had been overspending for several years, leading to the threat of a large programme overspend. It seemed as if all projects were spending up to budget if they could, while others were overspending because they had to. This was extremely frustrating for the investment planning staff. When individual projects applied for overspend requests, the paperwork invariably showed that it was caused by plausibly unavoidable events, such as a policy change, excavations striking bed rock or discoveries of contaminated land, protected species or items of archaeological interest.

Detailed investigations of specific overspending projects, which were extremely time consuming, revealed, however, that although some events resulted in savings, other choices had also been made that added scope and cost. While in many cases the extra scope was of value, it was unbudgeted and as a consequence there were other worthier local projects that were now unaffordable. It was in no one's interest to write off construction costs incurred against operational budgets when a project overspent, and it was never clear whose fault these overspends were.

As a consequence of local government changes, it became necessary at this point for network ownership of a large part of the region to be shared with an adjacent network owner. The existing operational and construction organisation continued to provide services to its new client. A clear commercial interface was created between the new network-owning organisation and the existing construction, delivery and operational business. Quite quickly, the new regional network owner insisted it would *only pay for approved project scope, and it required its junior staff to ensure scope was clear and defined in writing. Furthermore, it insisted it would not pay for work that was not formally agreed in the detail of the scope.*

This meant any extra scope would have to be funded by the budgets of the construction and operations organisation. It took several months for this change to become established. During this time new construction work stopped, due to extensive delays in the asset owner and asset operator agreeing the very detailed scopes. As a consequence, operational managers had craftsman with insufficient work to do, all overtime was stopped and efficiency abruptly declined.

To the unions and the workforce, this seemed a clear case of management ineptitude, which led them to question the need for, and the motives behind, wage restraint and other changes to working practices they were being asked to consider. On previous occasions when operational construction teams had run short of work the board had called for the urgent approval of schemes that would invariably emerge some years later as a string of overspending projects. However, this time the boards of the two organisations had to discuss and resolve the issue of how project scope could be clearly defined at the outset and who should pay for overspending projects. A short period of grace followed, very detailed project scopes were introduced at approval stage and a clear contractual understanding emerged that the network operator would pay for the cost of any unapproved scope from it own budgets. The formal and organisational separation of Level 2 and Level 3 functions (see Figure 10.3) removed a sense of short- and long-term conflict which the board of the previous organisation had been unable to resolve.

This case study does not intend to suggest this approach is best practice; such organisational interfaces also introduce cost. However, this approach can be highly effective at quickly bringing about complex change.

11.5   Conclusions

Strong **teams** and effective team working are necessary for the efficient and effective operation of utility organisational structures. At board level, it is likely the executive **team** for a utility will be equally represented with directors who can champion regulatory, asset management, operational and construction issues if need be. It is critical this team works as an effective team or at less senior levels it will be extremely unlikely utility staff representing each of these different disciplines to come together on a particular issue and operate as a comfortable and mature **team.**

Good team working can improve the performance of any business. However even with a strong leadership team, in a complex utility that is under pressure and has both a complex **organisation** and poor **tools**, the good faith of teams working on contentious issues can become stretched to breaking point. Under such circumstances, disputes and poor decision-making can arise, leading to wasted potential and poor performance. All utilities have experienced many such events and in a performance culture the challenge is to ensure the maximum amount of constructive tension is held in the business.

We have explored the key points of constructive tension within a modern utility. We then reviewed the survey results of utility departmental perceptions, which revealed the three areas where differing internal perceptions and values most often exist. These three areas are:

1. **Asset data and information:** There is recognition in operations and asset management that asset managers do not have the information they need to do their work well. However, it is frequently the case that all parties believe it is for others to resolve this issue.

2. **Quick provision of funding and policy changes:** There is a shared view in many utilities that asset management is not

able to provide urgently needed funding and policy changes quickly. Again, all parties believe others need to resolve this issue. It may be that asset managers blame regulators, while operational and construction staff blame asset managers.

3. **Visibility of programmes of work:** Construction staff do not believe they have sufficiently early visibility of programmes of work to enable them to do their work well. In general, asset management staff are unaware of the depth of this feeling.

There are many examples of individuals and groups of people in utilities with strongly held opposing views on important issues. Unsatisfied expectations and divergent opinions are clearly unhelpful in promoting team working. Understanding these issues, which all utilities face to varying degrees, can help to unlock considerable unexploited potential and remove unnecessary and unconstructive tension at little cost. The challenge for utility leaders is to ensure their executive team is as effective as possible at finding these issues and seeking resolution.

In addition to developing **tools** and **organisations** that manage constructive tension, leaders have also drawn on a number of concepts to promote team working. These include aligning **teams** to address common **goals**, such as health and safety or asset risk management, or to achieve previously enjoyed upper-quartile performances. A second range of strategies involves the use of **tools** to ensure tensions can be resolved through the rational discussion of issues.

Excellent team working is arguably the most important factor in the asset management capability model at enabling effectiveness and efficiency. This is because **teams** also build the **organisation** and design and implement the **tools** a utility uses.

12 Conclusions

In Chapter 1 we set out on our journey to understand why, and how, different utilities are implementing the different types of asset management systems they feel are appropriate.

Thirty years ago the term 'asset management' was not used in the utility sector. At this time utilities across the world were run in a predominantly reactive and budget constrained manner by local experts who often knew, from experience, what work they felt needed to be done. In recent years utilities have been developing 'asset management systems' to allow performance, risk and cost to be managed in a more formal manner. An objective of this book has been to share practical examples of what asset management means for a range of leading utilities, and how a range of people and technical issues have been addressed in these organisations.

In Chapter 1 we sought to understand how utility leaders and stakeholders could see into the extraordinary complexity of modern utilities and ensure both efficiency and effectiveness are delivered. We explored the Institute of Asset Management's definition of the asset management system, which may be used to do this. We also defined the asset management capability model, which holds the three factors that define how good an asset management system needs to be (climate, complexity and goals), and the three factors which together give it a degree of capability (tools, organisation and teams). We returned to this model throughout the book, as we sought to understand what types of asset management systems are appropriate, and how they can be established and organised.

We explored the history of utilities in Chapter 2. We noted that in their earliest stages, utilities were dynamic, privately owned pioneering businesses. Visionary engineers and businesspeople managed enormous risks and challenges. The benefits of delivering power, heat and light to households and factories for the first time, introducing mass transport and massively reducing infant mortality allowed some of the most imaginative engineering projects to be conceived or commissioned. As the methods of provision of utility services become better understood and the public began to view access to utility services as a right, rather than a luxury, the tone of the industry changed.

Regulation of standards of service, and price controls and other measures were introduced to control these natural monopolies. In this way, the utility industries moved into a 'lowest cost operation' regime, with a view, quite rightly, of ensuring the interests of the most vulnerable were protected. In many cases, this has lead to utility services moving into public ownership and control. This process has repeated itself from time to time as new utility services are created, or re-built. Indeed, this process may be underway in many countries to this day, as new utility services, such as the internet, become established.

More recently, however, society's values have begun to change. This is most clearly illustrated by the changing health and safety expectations of gas industry staff. Case study 2 in chapter 2 noted that the life expectancy of town gas coking plant staff in the 1830's was no more than eight years from when they began this work. In our modern society, the cost of preventing gas explosions in customers' properties may equate to many millions of euros per life saved. These changes are reflected in the wave of investment and modernisation of global utilities that is currently occurring, as climatic change, carbon emissions, water quality and customer safety issues are addressed. These extra pressures also create new conflicts, for instance, a new waste water treatment project may only improve river water quality through processes that consume power and other resources – which threaten to aggravate climatic change.

Three issues are common to all utility sectors in the mature economies. These are:

1. **A history of adaptation and re-engineering:** over their often-long histories, utilities have been re-engineered continually, and adapted to suit new requirements. All utilities, however, are largely composed of ageing assets into which complex modern systems and processes have been embedded.

2. **A trend for consolidation:** Across the world, almost all utility services started life as a local system serving a particular neighbourhood. With time, the growing complexity and need for greater efficiency has resulted in considerable consolidation of utility services. In some sectors, such as gas, consolidation has occurred worldwide, precipitated by the re-engineering of old networks to enable the evolution from town gas to natural gas. In other utility sectors, political or legal restrictions have prevented consolidation. The economic pressure for consolidation remains, and as utilities become more complex the need for, and barriers to, consolidation are becoming greater.

3. **Utility networks shaped by their history:** Even where consolidation has occurred, utilities continue to carry the hallmarks of their history. Different design approaches and collections of non-standardised assets make maintenance and operation of ageing networks more difficult. Furthermore, the location of key assets close to water – either because land was cheap, it gave good access to raw or cooling waters or it allowed waste waters to be discharged – now means critical infrastructure is often highly vulnerable to climatic change.

Utilities in the younger economies are experiencing similar pressures but for different reasons. The introduction of a wide range of complex modern utility services is in itself an exceptional challenge. Not only is the cost of these systems enormous, which means political and media oversight is significant, but maintaining services to existing (and, very often, the most wealthy and influential) customers while these large new projects are commissioned is a demanding, sensitive and often thankless exercise.

In order to help utilities seek additional funding from the capital markets, and sometimes to drive greater efficiency, governments across the world are seeking to introduce new forms of regulation. Chapter 3 summarised the key principles and outcomes from a range of different regulatory regimes across the world.

Chapter 4 looked at the scale and nature of the different utility sectors. The replacement values of the assets used by different sectors were explored, as was the make up of typical household bills in developed countries. Chapters 2, 3 and 4 should provide experienced utility staff with an informative summary of utility practice. These chapters may be of particular interest to utility staff who have not worked in a variety of utility sectors or geographies. These chapters are principally intended to give readers who are new to the utility sector an insight into the extraordinary complexity, scale and challenges facing modern utilities.

Utilities typically own £10m of tired and aged assets for every member of staff. As many of these assets are relatively low value, located above and below ground and stretching across huge areas, the practicalities of operating, maintaining and updating these systems are obvious. It we add a requirement that individual assets must be operated and maintained at minimal cost, with high availability for their service lives of between 10 to 200 years and with replacement only at the very last possible moment, the brinkmanship approach of the utility industry becomes clear.

Utility staff working across the world know that their work is worthwhile and important. This passion and commitment is invaluable in times of crisis, fire or storm. However, it also means every group of craftsmen, technicians and managers has strong views on what work should be done when, by whom and how. Harnessing this energy in these complex organisations in a practical and thoughtful way is the greatest challenge utilities face.

In Chapter 5, we explored the emerging need utilities have for asset management systems to see and manage risk and value in their complex businesses. We also returned to the asset management

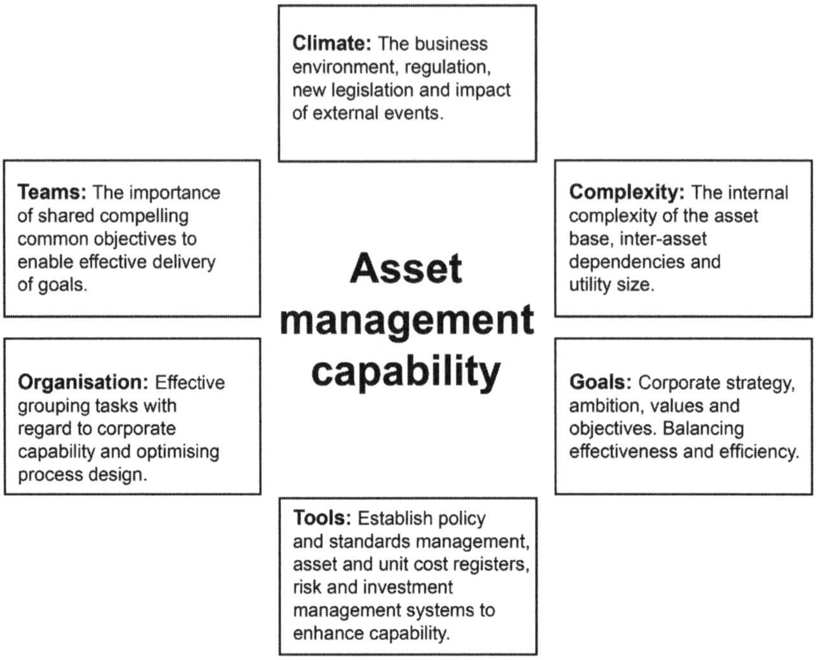

Figure 1.2 The asset management capability model

capability model, and prepared to explore each of its factors in the next six chapters.

We also explored the strategic significance of data in a modern utility. Data can be thought of as the 'machine code' of a utility. It is the building block of information and, ultimately, knowledge. Every asset inspection, repair, or investment project is initiated by information or data and as these transactions proceed, more data is created. By keeping (and discarding) the right data in the right way, and with the right associations between different fragments of data, the six factors in the asset management capability model can work together to find the right balance appropriate for a particular utility.

In Chapter 6, we explored the nature and significance of the first of the six factors included in the asset management capability model: **climate**. For utilities, the climate is the business environment in which the utility operates and is the equivalent of the market and economic environment within which a traditional trading business operates. The types of factors that determine the business climate a utility operates in include the tone of economic and quality regulation, the growth rate or degree of re-engineering that the utility asset base requires and its reputation. We explored the different climates that different utility sectors are exposed to in different parts of the world. We also looked at the features that determine the tone of regulation in Figure 6.1. The significance of climate is that the utilities operating in the most challenging climates have the greatest need for highly capable asset management systems. In contrast, utilities operation is a benign climate, where annual non-binding budgets and outcomes are acceptable to stakeholders, and there is little benefit in going to the trouble and cost of establishing a capable asset management system.

In Chapter 7 we examined utility complexity. A major determination of complexity is utility size. For very small utilities, and in this context that may be utilities serving less than 30,000 customers, it is possible for a small, highly experienced operational team that has a great deal of local knowledge to have a subjective view of where risk lies and what needs to be done next. If stakeholders are happy with such a regime (a benign climate) these businesses have little need for a formal asset management system. Above that size, however, the complexity of even the simplest type of utility makes proactive utility management and medium-term planning impossible without some elements of a formal asset management system. As utilities grow in size, and complexity, the types of responses necessary become harder to identify. This may be partly because decision makers become increasingly separated from day-to-day work and partly because the organisation faces larger numbers of risks and has more opportunities to address them effectively.

In addition to size, different utility industries have different inherent complexities. Although all utilities are complex compared with many other industries and most utilities operate a number of several extremely complex types of assets some utility sectors have greater numbers of unpredictable assets than others. These complex asset types can interact with each other, to create a semi-chaotic asset system which is hard to manage effectively without high levels of contingency. For example, waste water utilities are some of the most complex utility systems. This is because they use many buried old non standardised assets, biological processes (which are sensitive to temperature and inhibition), and networks which are buffeted by a range of weather and customer events.

The significance of complexity is it makes the type of response necessary to a particular challenge harder to identify. In the absence of complexity, the response to a challenging climate is clear. It might not be easily delivered, but at least the form of the response is clear. So, for example, gas distribution is an example of a utility that operates in a highly challenging climate by virtue of the ever-present health and safety concerns (due to high explosion risk) in everything it does. Compared to other utilities, it is not a complex utility and, accordingly, its response to pressures is clear and consistent: ensure delivery of excellent operational control and rigour in everything it does. Every pipe weld, every customer visit, every GIS record needs to be undertaken with the knowledge that if an error is made, an explosion could occur in a property.

The challenge of operating in this regime is highly demanding, but at least the nature of the response necessary is clear. There are two practical consequences of this which are relevant for all utilities but are particularly import for the most complex utilities. These are:

1. **Implementing asset management systems is hard:** The most complex utilities have greater challenges in implementing capable asset management systems. But if they are able to do so, they may also enjoy the most significant benefits. By contrast, the most capable asset management systems are often found amongst the leading utilities operating less-complex utility systems.

2. **More complex organisational design:** Complex utilities have a greater need for specialist skills and services and, occasionally, a range of specialist technical departments. This, in turn, can create more organisational interfaces and

an even greater need for better asset management systems and excellent team working to ensure the organisation does not confuse itself with its own complexity.

In Figure 7.5 at the conclusion of Chapter 7, we brought together the benchmarking of utility sector climate undertaken in Chapter 6 with the work in Chapter 7. By using the matrix illustrated earlier in Figure 7.2, those utility sectors experiencing the greatest need for highly capable asset management systems can be identified. Similarly, those utility sectors that by virtue of their exceptional complexity experience the greatest challenge in introducing highly capable asset management systems are identified. However, it is important to put some of these conclusions into perspective. Compared with other industries, all utilities utilise enormous numbers of disparate and critical assets, under a care and maintenance basis. Even canals and waterways – which are stable, low-complexity utility systems compared with other utilities – must be treated with the greatest care and respect. It is not unusual for a canal embankment to be supporting thousands, if not millions, of tonnes of water.

In Chapter 8, we explored the goals that utilities and their stakeholders choose as appropriate, with a special emphasis on efficiency and effectiveness. The goal of high efficiency can be achieved by intelligently restricting inputs, and effectiveness by skilfully managing outcomes. We noted well-managed larger utilities find it easier to excel at achieving frontier efficiency while the best smaller utilities find achieving exceptional effectiveness, such as excellent service, easier. We noted the challenge for any business is to grow its capability to achieve higher performance in both of these goals.

One enabler for achieving this objective is to grow the capability of the utility's asset management systems. The underlying economies of scale of maximising utility size are substantial. For example, studies in the US[1] have shown consolidation of water treatment and

---

[1] Congressional Budget Office Report, Drinking Water and Waste water Infrastructure, November 2002.

monitoring costs per customer can be reduced 75 times by consolidating smaller companies into utilities serving 500,000 people. Building utilities that are so large they are unmanageable, however, is a risk that must be addressed by developing appropriate asset management systems.

In Chapter 9, we examined tools, the fourth of the six factors in the asset management capability model. Tools enable utility leaders and managers to see and manage value in their organisations by understanding asset risk, impact and likelihood. Figure 9.1 outlined the architecture of a typical utility asset management system. The key elements of any system are to ensure there is a 'line of sight' from investment objectives to the individual investment projects and maintenance work that is undertaken on a daily basis.

In practice, this is undertaken by a series of tools that operate at varying strategic levels. In order for these tools to work together, integration is critical. This is undoubtedly the most difficult issue to address and is, quite often, an unwelcome constraint, which different groups of utility staff will resist if the need is not explained to them. Integration is achieved at the tactical level by defining a written asset data hierarchy and at the policy level by defining policy and plan hierarchies. Investment management tools, programme management and approval tools are also common resources that need to be shared by many groups to ensure objectives and processes are clear.

In section 9.7, we noted that different asset management planning tools are used to prepare top-down investment plans and bottom-up investment proposals. The tools used to produce these proposals are very different in character – top-down tools are fed by a general knowledge of all assets, while bottom-up tools are driven by localised facts, events and issues. Top-down tools are useful for setting budgets, securing funding, setting affordable objectives and combining these issues into medium- and long-term plans. They are highly pro-active and help clarify the whole picture. In contrast, bottom-up tools drive day-to-day investment and operational interventions. They typically tell us a great deal about a particular issue. Some types of bottom-up information (such as lists of failed equipment that require immediate repair) are easy to interpret.

However, much bottom-up information is constituted of long lists of worthwhile projects, some of which is important but most is unaffordable and poor value. The approaches utilities use to enhance the capabilities of these two types of tools were discussed in Figure 9.10. The gap between them must be addressed with a range of informal reviews and systems. Figure 9.11 characterised several approaches which leading companies have used to bridge this gap. With time, as data and expertise grows, the decision-making gap is closing in most utilities. Even the most complex utilities have some assets of a criticality and complexity where there is little gap between the top-down planning and the bottom-up prioritisation systems. However, expert human oversight of all planning and prioritisation systems is always needed and utility complexity means it is unlikely to ever be practical to deploy fully predictive planning and prioritisation systems for many types of assets. Accordingly, it is best to think of tools removing as much 'clutter' in the asset planning and decision-making processes as possible, so staff can concentrate on the most challenging issues.

The most sophisticated and effective tools are generally found in the highly stressed industries (see Figures 7.2 and 7.5). In the power generation industry, leading companies integrate real-time process risk and operational scheduling within monthly and yearly capex and opex investment budgeting and planning. These are examples of the Type 4 tools included in Figure 9.11.

However, most utilities operate many types of assets whose real-time risk and performance control is either not possible or not viable. Leading companies operating such assets are deploying condition-based predictive tools that not only prioritise investment options effectively, but also use scenario modelling to predict future network performance and risk for different investment strategies. Such tools are examples of Type 3 decision-support processes (see Figure 9.11), as used in electricity and rail utilities. In order to undertake this, these utility sectors have had to collect large amounts of information of particular assets and short segments of track. The gas industry, which has the challenge of managing some of the most critical underground assets, has been highly innovative and rigorous in the early deployment of Type 2 and Type 3 systems to address current and future explosion risk. The water and, in particular, waste water industries have successfully deployed leading processes on their critical and visible assets, such as impounding reservoirs, incinerators and UV disinfection plants. However the water, and particularly waste water sectors face two challenges that make wide-scale deployment of leading asset management practice slow, and sometimes unviable. Firstly, many network and process assets are buried and hard to inspect. Secondly, as noted earlier these utility sectors operate large numbers of complex chemical and biological processes, which are prone to inhibition and vulnerable to many types of weather events making performance hard to model. The growing sophistication and automation of these processes, however, creates richer real-time data from which risk, cost and performance can be assessed. The next challenge for these industries is to complete the implementation of comprehensive real-time network and process control. The data generated by these systems will allow the wide-scale implementation of Type 3 and Type 4 asset management systems and decision-support processes.

It should be noted, however, that these industry generalisations are over-simplifications because different assets require different responses. It is a legal requirement in most countries for lifting devices and pressure vessels to be managed with Type 3 decision-support processes. Conversely the use of complex decision-support processes to manage, for example, the replacement of light bulbs is clearly inappropriate in any business. In establishing appropriate tools, it is essential to avoid complexity that is economically unviable. Any one of these tools, taken to an extreme, could bankrupt a utility. Accordingly, control of the scope to ensure simplicity is valued.

A key point to note is a utility's asset management system seeks to give 'a line of sight' and not 'a line of control'. Experienced staff are needed at every level to manage and control issues. For this reason, the last two elements of the asset management system, organisation and teams, are the most important.

In Chapter 10, we noted that the growing need for greater utility efficiency and effectiveness means traditional utility organisational structures, led by local operational experts, are less appropriate. Modern organisational structures place more emphasis on regulation, planning, and benefits and risk management, as utility managers must achieve and demonstrate excellent value in their work to stakeholders. This is not to say operational excellence is less important. It does mean, however, that utilities need to hold much more complex pressures within them, and this requires excellent tools and new organisational approaches.

There is no 'best' organisational approach. Many different modern organisational approaches can be made to work well. Indeed, the process of change from one organisational approach to another is helpful in stimulating growth, efficiency and change. In Chapter 10, Figure 10.3, we broke the more strategic element of a typical utility's asset management system into 12 functional groups. Depending on the size and nature of a utility, each of those functional groups could vary in size from a part-time task for one person to a large department. These groups can be packaged together into organisational structures in a variety of different ways. We noted there is value in recognising that certain functional groups operate on different strategic levels, and recognising this in an organisational design can help establish a performance culture. This is because, under a regime of constructive tension, there is less scope for strategic decision making to be made solely with a view to achieving a particular tactical benefit. In Figure 10.4 we categorised the 12 functional groups into four groupings as follows:

- Level 1: Establishing objectives and funding
- Level 2: Deciding how to achieve objectives
- Level 3: Preparing and organising for asset operation and construction

- Level 4: Commissioning, operating, repairing, constructing and decommissioning assets.

Broadly, the Level 1 grouping reflects regulatory management and financial modelling; Level 2 incorporates departments with names such as 'asset management' or 'network strategy'. Level 3 groupings are those parts of operations or construction management that organise and control their activities. Together, these groupings, and the constituent 12 functional groups from which they are composed, control and direct a utility's asset management system.

The controlling nature of the Level 1 and 2 groupings means the highest levels of effectiveness are critical for these activities. For the other organisational groupings, the greatest challenge is frontier efficiency. We noted how important it is, for the organisation as a whole, to respect and support these goal priorities. We also explored the importance of carefully managing the interfaces between different functional groups and we explored the use of a range of tools, such as project and programme approval processes, in doing so.

In Chapter 11, we looked at the most powerful and defining of the three factors that deliver asset management capability, teams and team working. Great team working and relationship management allow resources to be assigned to the most important work, irrespective of organisational design. Organisational structures can allow specialisation, which increases efficiency and effectiveness. However, as one business leader reflected in case study 1 in chapter 11:

'A key challenge is to overcome tribalism, with individual teams only focused on trying to do their job. At best, it leads to everyone thinking they have done a great job but the poor outcome is someone else's fault.'

Delivering team working within a team is comparatively easy because the team members all work for their leader. The challenge is to prevail on the team leader to be sensitive to other departmental needs, and this becomes more important with rising organisational complexity and greater numbers of interfaces. Narrow thinking can result in the organisation's decision making processes becoming choked if the correct tools aren't there to make the facts clear and, likewise, if the right behaviours to allow conflict to be reconciled for the greater good are also missing.

In Chapter 11, the results of an earlier qualitative survey of the causes of conflict within utilities (which was discussed in Figure 9.5) were used as the basis for a more searching review of how well different organisational groupings were able to support each other. Even though many of the utilities participating in this review were leading utilities, this survey revealed considerably different views on the same important issues within the best organisations. In itself, the disparate views held within the same organisation on the same issue illustrate the leadership challenges in complex organisations. A number of significant trends emerged by averaging the results for all organisations. The summary of this review is included in Figure 11.2. The three key concussions were:

1. **Asset information and data**: there is often a broad recognition that staff planning and organising did not have sufficient asset information to do this work well. Frequently, there is a view that it is for others to resolve this issue.
2. **Providing funding and updating asset policy**: construction and operational staff do not feel asset management staff are able to discharge this duty well. Interestingly, asset managers often agree and this is an area for more research.
3. **Visibility of future work**: construction staff do not feel they have early enough visibility of programmes of work, and asset managers may not appreciate the strength of feeling on this issue.

The above conclusions are the averages of the views of many different leaders and managers working in a wide range of utilities. There is evidence senior leaders may be more concerned, or oblivious, than their staff on different issues. What is more interesting is that even within excellent utilities operating successfully under the leadership of respected leaders in challenging economic climates, the three behavioural fault-lines detailed above are still found.

In any utility, every one of us is in a position of taking short-term actions that help us to achieve our immediate objectives, but which may make other people's work harder to do well. Too much short-term thinking makes long-term high performance of the organisation as a whole impossible.

The language that helps us all work co-operatively is data and information. We all know this, and yet few utilities feel they manage information as well as they would wish, and we all seem to think it is someone else's job to sort it out. For those of us is in positions of power, such as regulators and business leaders, we must show we value information, and use it for something other than justifying a decision not to fund something. For those of us planning and prioritising work, we need to be clear about exactly what information and data we really need. For those of us designing and running information systems, we have to resist the urge to put in 'one last really enormous information system' which, 'in one giant leap', will solve all our problems. For those of us operating, maintaining and constructing new assets we have a role to look after, collect and maintain information and data. And, in return, expect excellent and responsive support from the rest of the organisation.

So, have we found the secret formula for great asset management? No. We have identified a number of approaches that have been used sucessfully by leading utilities on their own paths towards excellence. The art and challenge of asset management and utility leadership is to implement planned change and improvement. There are no short cuts which everyone has overlooked. Progress can only start if we are unsatisfied with the situation in which we find ourselves. Given that three-quarters of utilities consider themselves to be above average for a utility, this satisfaction with the status quo isn't always deserved. We are only likely to set out on the path to excellence if we are ambitious and believe that the search will be fruitful. The leading utilities are working towards zero interruptions of service to their customers, perfect service punctuality or more fault-free days across their networks. Finally, a search for anything challenging and worthwhile is a journey past many distractions and dead ends. False trails may be convenient for some groups within the utility organisations, but overall they destroy value by making other people's work much harder.

By following the approaches and principles detailed in this book, any utility can establilsh the asset management structures and tools that are necessary if the business is to deliver excellent utility performance. However, the successful and cost-effective implementation of many of these ways of working is hard, and there are always further enhancements and improvements that can add value. However, starting change is easier than successfully concluding it. The really great utility leadership teams recognise that the quest for utility excellence requires vision, tenacity and attention to detail over a longer period than the average two to three years that an individual senior executive stays in the same role.

Appendix 1

[Company name]
POLICY Level 1

Title:	Asset Data and Information			Ref:	EW.10
Business Owner:	Asset Management Director	Date Produced:	27/02/10	Review Date:	08/02/13

1. Purpose:

- To ensure appropriate and affordable asset data and address/connection data is collected, maintained, made available to and used by the business.
- For the purpose of this policy asset data and information includes regulatory information and reports, details of the location (property address), condition, performance and type of assets and appropriate unit costs for the whole life of the asset. It shall include all forms of raw data collection, management, measurement and storage regardless of the form or format.

2. Policy Statement:

- Asset data shall be held and maintained on corporate systems. A list of systems deemed to be 'corporate' shall also be maintained by the C Band manager responsible for information systems.
- As a preference asset data shall be maintained by staff who are as close as practicable to the activity which has resulted in a change to our asset data records, and the requirements for data collection shall be clearly defined in an individual's roles and responsibilities. If backlogs of asset data updates can be tolerated backlog size must be managed and reported.
- Asset data shall be collected once only and mastered, stored and structured in the format specified by the Asset Data Hierarchy (ADH) and made available to other corporate systems and applications.
- Contractors will not be paid for services until they have satisfied any data maintenance/update requirements.
- Data quality measures shall be established and maintained to ensure the integrity of the data to agreed standards. This will include a presentation to the board by the B Band Manager responsible for asset strategy at 12 month intervals on the effectiveness of Asset Registration/Deregistration Processes and update backlogs in all areas with a comparison with previous year's performance.
- Asset information shall be made freely available to staff and all reasonable measures shall be taken to help staff have confidence in the accuracy of asset data.
- The use of parallel paper systems and the extraction of asset data into standalone databases or spreadsheets which become maintained shall be discouraged and prior approval from the D band manager responsible for asset data strategy shall be required. When this activity is approved it may also be required that proposals be agreed and funded to ensure this information shall be put back into a corporate system at the end of the activity by the project or department which manages the activity. The D Band Manager responsible for asset Data strategy shall annually refresh the list of useful asset data mastered on non corporate systems to identify unapproved data sets and review this list with the C Band manager responsible for Information Systems.

<table>
<tr><td>[Company logo]</td><td align="right">[Company name]
POLICY Level 1</td></tr>
</table>

3. Policy Background:

- Poor data maintenance can lead to corruption of asset data, which results in poor decision making and expensive and time-consuming repeated resurveying of assets
- Asset data and information which is reported to the Regulator must be prepared and used with utmost diligence
- The company has a duty to keep a formal record and inventory of its assets and this policy ensures that this duty can be discharged

4. Interrelationships With Other Documentation

Parent Documentation:	Interrelated Documentation:	Impacted Documentation:
	<ul><li>Data Audit Policy</li><li>Water Network Modelling Policy</li><li>Asset Management Policy</li><li>Asset Data Hierarchy (ADH)</li></ul>	<ul><li>Effective Maintenance Policy</li><li>Asset Surveys Policy</li><li>Regulatory Data Capture Policy</li><li>Principles of Data Management Policy</li></ul>

5. Target:

- To ensure the correct data is available in order to provide high quality information to support optimal asset management
- Secure and keep the Regulator's approval and confidence in the quality and appropriateness of our asset data and information
- Ensure confidence grades for regulation reports are rigorously prepared and all reasonable steps shall be taken to avoid deterioration on previous submissions' reported confidence grades
- For regulatory reporting asset data and information methodologies shall be documented and owners of data used to create regulatory reports shall confirm due care and attention has been used
- To constrain data management cost to a level compatible with the value generated by the data

---

[Company logo]

[Company name]
POLICY Level 1

---

6. Risks, Issues and Constraints:

- The business and its stakeholders require very high levels of data accuracy and substantive challenges and penalties can result if these high levels are missed
- Asset data and information is typically collected disparately by many people undertaking different activities over extended periods of time. It is then aggregated to form investment plans and regulatory reports. If these reports are to be appropriate, systematic errors or unknown omissions in large numbers of peoples' work must be avoided.
- When deciding if it is necessary to collect a new asset dataset it shall be recognised that half of the whole life cost of data is data maintenance

7. Key Words:

Asset; Data; Information; Report; ADH

Approved By	Name	Date	Signature
Prepared by			
[committee name] Forum			
[committee members]			
[committee members]			
[committee members]			
[committee members]			
[committee members]			

Amendment Summary

Amendment No. Date	Issue	Brief Description and Amending Action
18-01-10	0	Final Issue for [company name] Board approval
23-02-10	1	Approved policy

Appendix 2

Examples of the titles of the Level 1 asset management policy documents for an electricity distribution utility

For illustrative purposes a one line summary of the types of policy approaches a company may pursue is included for each policy area. Policy areas are chosen either by virtue of their gravity (health & safety) or because they are issues identified in the regulatory contract and so drive regulatory funding, incentives and compliance reporting.

Customer service: Ensure and demonstrate asset standards and operational policy reflect the whole cost of associated customer services and customer disruption.

Health & Safety: Reference to corporate policy and implementation approach.

Serviceability: Maintain the overall fault rates for equipment at current levels. Define exactly what 'current levels' means. Ensure regulator accepts this definition. Take additional measures to reduce the impact of faults on customers.

Reinforcement: Define the measures which determine current levels of risk and the required risk reduction from reinforcement schemes. Outline the process which ensures investment plans address regulatory and licence condition issues.

Customer Interruptions and Customer Minutes Lost: Operational and investment objectives and approach for responding to this incentive scheme.

Fault Restoration Costs: Deliver x% reduction in the total capex and opex costs for fault restoration and repair.

Regulatory measures: Approach to guaranteed standards and other regulatory measures.

Asset management policy: Approach to developing tools, measuring capability, stimulating innovation and improvement and quality standards such as PAS 55.

Data and information management: Principles.

Regulatory and statutory obligations: Satisfy all such existing obligations and resist new obligations without first securing regulatory funding.

Maintenance & inspection regime: Basket of measures to ensure delivery. Define monitoring regime and exception reporting and actions.

Out performance against regulatory contract: Objectives for all Investment programmes (opex and all separate capex programmes including non operational capex).

Connections: Ensure value for money and customer service is measured and clear.

Research and development investment: Approach to R & D and principles.

Overheads and recharges: Definition and proposals and plans.

Distributed generation: Basis for supporting and promoting.

Climatic change and flooding: Basis for addressing and promoting.

Other issues, such as skills retention and development, are key Board Agenda items and operation of the asset management system depends on these issues. However they can be sponsored and directed outside the asset management system. PAS 55 details a useful description of the scope of the asset management system.

Appendix 3

The key functional groups which control a utility's asset management system

Functional group	Accountability and purpose
Economic Regulation	This function is accountable for ensuring the business agrees a regulatory contract with the key funding stakeholders who, for utilities, may be local government or economic regulators. This is achieved by taking the internally approved investment plans and presenting them to the economic regulator. In most cases this will mean Economic Regulation is accountable for interactions with the economic regulator. However, for unregulated utilities the function may involve liaison with local government, customers and other key funding stakeholders. A key challenge is to understand the requirements of and the pressures experienced by regulators and ensure proposals presented to them reflect these sensitivities as much as is possible. This will allow the business to be responsive to regulatory requirements but challenging when appropriate and ensure the business understands and accommodates these requirements.
Corporate Finance	This function is accountable for accessing the financability and fundability of regulatory and rate and tariff proposals. It has a right of veto on any investment plans or proposals. The activity is a sub set of the corporate and financial management of the organization.
Investment Management	Investment Management hold the high level 'master plan' or investment plan for proposals, outputs and regulatory performance measures of agreed regulatory contracts. The investment plans will be for the duration of the regulatory contract and it will have a focus on outturn costs and outputs. Investment Management's purpose is to bridge any gap between internal plans and financial budgets and the regulatory contract and so ensure value (not just money) is controlled. It is critical it provides excellent service to, and maintains the trust of, Finance, Economic Regulation, and all other functional groups preparing investment proposals and plans. To do so an approach which avoids being judgemental but is observational is helpful. It may be deciding little but it will be summarising the logical conclusions of all investment options prepared by Corporate Finance, Quality Regulation, Asset Replacement Planning and Supply/Demand Planning.
Quality Regulation	This function is accountable for all interactions with all quality regulators on issues such as environmental licensing, water abstraction, cooling water reuse and quality of supply issues. If quality regulators and economic regulators are not working together this function can become very important to ensure unfunded obligations are not accepted and this function can become a Level 1 task. When quality regulatory reporting results in many transactions the day to day activates may be delegated. A key challenge is to understand the requirements of and the pressures experienced by quality regulators. This will allow it to be responsive to regulatory requirements but challenging when appropriate and ensure the business understands and can accommodate these requirements.
Asset Replacement Planning (Maintenance Planning)	This function is accountable for sponsoring capex, opex and refurbishment initiatives which are within the agreed constraints held in the agreed investment plan and which ensure that the existing operational asset base continues to function in an acceptable manner. In some industries the term Capital Maintenance Planning is used to describe this activity. It will own and direct the operation of the asset risk management processes the business uses for quantifying the service risk from failure of assets and preparation of the investment programs needed to control this risk. This function must have a deep knowledge of the asset base, failure modes, criticality, capability and consequences of equipment failures and causes of wear and ageing. It will work closely with Operations and Capital Delivery Planning functions to ensure optimised operational and investment proposals are developed.

Enhancement Planning (Supply/ Demand and Reinforcement)	This function is accountable for sponsoring initiatives which are required to enhance the performance or capacity of the asset system, such as environmental improvement schemes, rail safety or capacity work, and reinforcement and supply/demand investment. Examples of issues it must address include responding to new regulatory standards (including specific health and safety drivers), new connections, reinforcement arising from new connections and construction of new capacity. The programmes of work it sponsors must satisfy any constraints held in the agreed investment plans. The maintenance and running of models, determining points of connection, demand forecasting and sponsoring projects through complex construction programmes are key tasks.
Asset Policies and Standards	This function is accountable for ensuring all asset policy and standards are created, published and maintained in accordance with the agreed governance. In practice this means for the most strategic documents (Level 1) the department is an administrative function. However, for all other documents for which it has the resources to do so it will chair consultation meetings and occasionally act as a company authority on the more strategic technical issues.
Strategic Asset Data	This function is accountable for the strategic management of asset data including static data, condition data, data definitions, unit costs data, and data hierarchies. This is likely to be a small function of several people and the majority of work will be undertaken by information system operators. Accordingly excellent team working and strong sponsorship is necessary.
Programme Management	This function is accountable for holding and maintaining the company's formal record of capex and repex projects under consideration and under investment. It must also ensure the plan is aligned with the investment plan, and accordingly allowances need to be held in the plan to accommodate unapproved but intended work. A major challenge is to establish the likely aggregate out turn cost of these programmes of work. It is also accountable for administering the capital approvals process. The function should not get involved in the management of individual projects, except when post investment appraisals are undertaken. This function must work closely with Investment Management and all planning functions to ensure it is rigorous but keeps and maintains the trust of all organizations. To do so an approach which avoids being judgmental but is observational is helpful.
Asset Operation & Maintenance Scheduling	This function is accountable for work scheduling and implementing agreed asset management policy, such as maintenance policy, operational policy, and repair and asset registration and de-registration policy, into operations. It is accountable for ensuring policy and plans accommodate the operational realities and experience. In this sense it is the 'brains' of operations and the key operational function which controls the asset management system. It will also undertake scheduling and work planning.
Asset Construction Planning	This function is accountable for preparing construction delivery plans which accommodate the requirements of the investment plan. It is also accountable for ensuring policy and plans accommodate practical hard constraints, such as the availability of contractor resources and planning permissions.
Pricing & Estimating	This function is accountable for establishing the cost of new assets, at the early stage of planning, for capital approvals and in the advances stages of delivery. In this way there is a sense of continuity between cost estimating for long term planning and actual project delivery.